Mathematics
and
Politics

Hayward R. Alker, Jr.

YALE UNIVERSITY

The Macmillan Company, New York
Collie

First Printing

Library of Congress catalog card number: 65-15593

THE MACMILLAN COMPANY, NEW YORK
COLLIER–MACMILLAN CANADA, LTD., TORONTO, ONTARIO

Printed in the United States of America

Preface

Writing a book about Mathematics and Politics means appealing to two potentially different audiences, whose interests have diverged from each other more than the historical originators of the subjects would have favored. Students of politics, whether they concentrate on facts or contemplate ideals, are now more frequently inclined to challenge the relevance of mathematical analysis to politics than were Pythagoras, Plato, or Aristotle. As taught to political scientists, mathematics often lacks the intellectual excitement of the original discoveries that have so closely linked much of the mathematical imagination with the social and natural world. Mathematical drudgery or a parochial approach to politics too often obscure the relevance of mathematics to the moral and empirical problems of political analysis.

This book is most emphatically not a "how-to-do-it" cookbook of statistics for political scientists. It does attempt to illustrate how several important ideas in the history of mathematics may increase our understanding of politics. To achieve this, we first need some idea of the nature of these two disciplines, the objects they study, and their historical interrelationships. In Chapter 1, mathematics is described as the logical study of quantitative and qualitative symbols. Its results are not valid because particular empirical interpretations seem appropriate. Rather, they follow necessarily from certain logical rules. Historically, however, mathematical political analysis has only gradually been disassociated from metaphysical views of the universe.

After a review of various definitions of politics and schemes of political analysis, Chapter 2 discusses related problems. Careful measurement procedures allow us to make empirical interpretations of content-free mathematical relationships.

Elaborating upon classical ideas of justice and political inequality, Chapter 3 exemplifies the usefulness of a mathematical approach to concept formation. The basic geometric idea responsible for generating various ways of describing inequality is the cumulative distribution, frequently referred to as the Lorenz curve. Inequalities in legislative apportionment, income tax structures, and racial educational opportunities are then described and evaluated using these concepts.

If political science is most directly concerned with the stating and testing of hypotheses relating clearly conceptualized variables, mathematical theories and techniques are likely to be appropriate. Chapters 4 through 6 review and compare various ways of formally stating and testing theories about politics, paying particular attention to the problem of distinguishing causal explanations from other statistical associations.

Several methods for studying the degree of association among qualitative attributes and quantitative variables are identified and illustrated in Chapter 4. Geometrical and algebraic identities between many of these measures

iii

are established using Galton's fundamental ideas of linear regression and correlation analysis. In all but one case, proofs are derived without requiring any knowledge beyond that acquired in two or three years of high school algebra and geometry, making many of the basic ideas of modern statistical analysis fully available to the non-mathematically trained student of politics.

Problems associated with ascertaining statistical "significance" of a testing procedure are relegated to a final appendix because the author finds that they are so often confused with the theoretical usefulness of regression and correlation analysis. Many of the appropriate techniques for generalizing from random samples of political data are thus not included in this book, although they are available in a good many textbooks written for economists or sociologists, of which those by Blalock, Suits, Wallis and Roberts, and Zelditch are among the author's favorites.*

Because political reality is complex, mathematical contributions to empirical political theory will eventually include those of multivariate (many-variable) statistics. Using a central result, which is proved using only high school algebra, known as the covariance theorem, Chapters 5 and 6 concentrate on the simple additive and multiplicative ways in which political phenomena can be mathematically explained. Lazarsfeld's contributions to the understanding of three-variable statistical relationships have been reviewed and developed into a more general analysis of fallacies common to political inference. Herbert Simon's extremely important distinctions between spurious correlations and causal relations have also been presented without any gaps in their mathematical derivations. Political scientists need not take on faith such important additions to the more standard regression techniques for multivariate analysis. Some of these elements of multivariate analysis will surely appear in future models of complex political processes now being made possible through the use of computer simulation techniques.

Finally, as an example of a different kind of moral and strategic analysis of rational choice in competitive situations, Chapter 7 presents a few of the major theorems of the von Neumann-Morgenstern theory of games. These important examples of deductive reasoning are then applied to current problems in normative and empirical political analysis.

Mathematics is satisfying because its results, however surprising, are logically certain; but its abstractions require careful attention to the details of logical argument, which cannot be as quickly absorbed as detective fiction. Once the reader understands the measurement concepts in Chapter 2, he will be able to read Chapters 3, 4, or 7. Chapters 5 and 6 rely considerably on some of the ideas developed in the earlier discussion (Chapter 4) of regression and correlation. Readers may therefore choose any of several strategies in going through this book, once the preliminary chapters have

* Hubert M. Blalock, Jr., *Social Statistics* (New York: McGraw-Hill, 1960); Daniel B. Suits, *Statistics: An Introduction to Quantitative Economic Research* (Chicago: Rand McNally, 1963); W. Allen Wallis and Harry V. Roberts, *Statistics: A New Approach* (New York: The Free Press of Glencoe, 1956); and Morris Zelditch, *A Basic Course in Sociological Statistics* (New York: Holt, Rinehart and Winston, 1959). Although it is no longer available as a text, V. O. Key's *A Primer of Statistics for Political Scientists* (New York: Crowell, 1959) also deserves special mention.

been mastered. For any of these, he may omit sections of greater than average difficulty without losing the basic line of argument.* The mathematical treatment of value distributions and strategic choice in Chapters 3 and 7 may attract those readers more inclined to normative analysis. Chapters 4 through 6 focus more heavily, but not exclusively, on mathematical relationships especially relevant to empirical theories of politics. Whether he takes either or both of these approaches, the reader is urged to explore the unifying mathematical concepts underlying much of recorded political experience.

Acknowledgements

My intellectual debts in writing this book are numerous. Among those scholars cited most frequently in the text are Paul Lazarsfeld, whose translations into social science language, with many extensions, of G. Udny Yule's work on the mathematics of attributes form the basis of several chapters in this book; John von Neumann and Oskar Morgenstern, authors of the classic *Theory of Games and Economic Behavior;* and Herbert Simon, whose *Models of Men* is perhaps the most impressive mathematical treatment of political problems that I have ever read.

Among my teachers and colleagues Robert Abelson, Hubert Blalock, Robert Dahl, Karl Deutsch, John Harsanyi, Robert Lane, Zvi Nammenwirth, and Harold Lasswell have all contributed in various ways to my understanding of mathematics and politics. Bruce Russett deserves special mention for his contributions to our earlier collaboration in defining and measuring politically relevant inequalities.

Those collecting the data used in this book are too numerous to mention individually. A collective word of thanks should be added, however, to the specific references in the text below.

Many others have alleviated the birth pains associated with the actual production of the final manuscript. The Yale Political Data Program has paid most of the salaries involved and shared with the Yale Computer Center the computational costs. Stephen Stephens and Douglas Condie have been helpful research assistants. My wife, Judith Ann Alker, and Norman Hix have joined in drawing the many graphs contained herein. Betsy Hendrix, Kay Latona, Louise Merelman, and Joan Amore have typed countless pages of strange symbols. Nelson W. Polsby, Elton Jackson, and especially Michael Leiserson have helpfully criticized earlier drafts. All of them have improved upon a work whose errors of omission and commission are clearly my own.

H.R.A.

---

* Paragraphs that on first reading may prove hard to understand are preceded by an asterisk (*).

Contents

CHAPTER 1

Mathematics and Politics: Some Historical Relationships

God always geometrizes

PLATO[1]

THE QUOTATION ABOVE suggests that the great political philosophers of antiquity held mathematics in high regard. In addition to their seminal roles in the Western philosophical tradition, both Plato and Aristotle played leading parts in the history of mathematics, Plato as an inspired teacher and Aristotle as the author of several complex treatises on mathematical logic. After a rudimentary history of mathematics, this chapter will illustrate several early uses of mathematics in political philosophy; then mathematics will be defined in a way that makes clear its relevance to politics. It should not be a surprising discovery that mathematics has strongly influenced the development of Western political thought.

A. Elements in the History of Mathematics

Derived literally from words meaning "to measure the earth," geometry is perhaps the oldest branch of mathematics. Egyptian surveyors used ropes with equally distant knots to measure out the land of the king, to reduce or increase taxes as a result of the wanderings of

---

[1] Found in Plutarch, this possibly apocryphal reply to a student's question, "What does God do?" is mentioned both by H. W. Turnbull and George Sarton as characteristic of Plato's view of the importance of mathematics. Another tradition is that the inscription above the door of the Academy was: "Nobody should enter who is not a mathematician." See H. W. Turnbull, "The Great Mathematicians," reprinted in James R. Newman, *The World of Mathematics* (New York: Simon and Schuster, 1956), Chapter I, pp. 75–168, especially pp. 95–96, and George Sarton, *A History of Science* (Cambridge: Harvard University Press, 1956), Volume 1, p. 432. Both of these multi-volume works have been helpful sources for the history of mathematics.

the Nile. Certainly the pyramids reveal a practical mastery of geometry, partly for political purposes.

PYTHAGOREAN MATHEMATICS. The Greeks, notably Thales and Pythagoras, added abstractness, generality, and intellectual respectability to Egyptian practical geometry. In particular, Pythagoras gave a fourfold meaning to the word "mathematics" (literally "of the form or character of knowledge"). Universal knowledge was possible about "discrete" or "continuous" objects: the objects of discrete knowledge were arithmetical (whole numbers) or musical (the notes of the scale). Continuous reality, on the other hand, was either constant or in motion; geometry and astronomy, respectively, were the appropriate mathematical disciplines.

Pythagorean arithmetic studied the properties of numbers, eternal objects symbolized by geometrical patterns of dots in the sand.[2] The flavor of his approach can be illustrated by his distinction between triangular and square numbers. "Triangular numbers" included 1, 3, 6, 10, while 4, 9, 16, etc., were "square numbers." Thus 9 and 10 were represented by

respectively. The latter figure, known as the *holy tetractys*, was a revered symbol among Pythagorean followers; besides providing a base for the decimal number system, it contains and is the sum of all the prior triangular numbers. Each of these numbers also had a mystical meaning, in somewhat the same manner that the Trinity of Christian theology refers to three different aspects of one God. Square numbers were equally susceptible to imaginative interpretations, as we shall see below.

Pythagoras and his followers were perhaps the first to consider music a branch of mathematics. The Greeks were aware of certain "natural" musical harmonies. On the piano we know of them today as chords, such as octaves (8 white keys apart), fourths (4 white keys apart), and fifths (5 white keys apart). For his musical studies, Pythagoras used an instrument known as the "monochord," consisting "of a single string stretched between rigid supports over a movable bridge, which rests in a sounding board. The length of the vibrating part of the string can be altered by moving the bridge."[3] Specifically, Pythagoras found that

[2] H. W. Turnbull, *op. cit.*, p. 84f.
[3] See Klaus Liepmann, *The Language of Music* (New York: Ronald Press, 1953), p. 46ff.

octaves are produced by vibrating strings with lengths in a ratio of 2:1, fifths result from 3:2 ratios, while fourths come from vibrating lengths in 4:3 proportions. Dissonances are produced by lengths not in simple numerical proportions to each other. Similar results for all kinds of instruments and all possible musical chords provided additional evidence for the Pythagorean belief that the underlying harmonies of the universe are all numerical.

Geometrically, of course, Pythagoras is remembered for his theorem equating in area the square on the hypotenuse of a right triangle to the sum of squares on the other two sides. This result led him to a less well known but mathematically important distinction between commensurable and incommensurable quantities. Mathematicians studying geometry and astronomy discovered quantities like π (the constant ratio between the circumference and the diameter of a circle) and $\sqrt{2}$ (the length of the diagonal of a square with sides of length 1), which could not be expressed using the whole numbers of arithmetic. Today "incommensurables" are known as "irrational numbers"—that is, they cannot be expressed as ratios of integers.[4]

ARISTOTLE'S SYLLOGISMS. Aristotle, a student of Plato, was the first to systematize what is commonly called "logical reasoning." For this purpose he developed a whole series of logical syllogisms, precursors of the propositions of modern mathematical logic. Because Aristotle was especially interested in reasoning logically about politics, and because he showed how to do so systematically, we now turn to this important chapter of the history of Greek mathematics.

To understand the syllogism, one should remember that Aristotle was interested in both inductive and deductive inferences, which mean, respectively, the processes of generalizing from particular facts to universal ones, and of deriving specific statements from more general ones. Statements of fact, in classical terminology, were predicates

[4] Pythagoras' discovery of irrational numbers provides insights into an important technique of mathematics: proof by contradiction. His surprising conclusion illustrates the power of mathematical reasoning in a manner similar to Arrow's impossibility theorem discussed in Chapter 7. Briefly, Pythagoras *assumed* the diagonal of a square to be a rational number, expressible in integer units, by which the side of the square was also measured. In his proof, he simplified all lengths as much as possible (so that they had no common divisors). He already knew from his theorem that the length of the diagonal squared equalled the sum of the squared length of each side, or twice the squared length of a side. But this meant that the squared length of the diagonal, and hence the diagonal itself, were even numbers, with a common divisor of 2! His original assumption had led to a contradiction, and was therefore wrong. Today we would say the diagonal (D) is related to the side (S) by the equation $D = S\sqrt{2}$.

asserted of particular objects.   Specifying the *extent* to which these predicates applied, Aristotle showed, is equivalent to quantifying the universality of "qualitative" judgments.

Typically, Aristotle worked with both specific examples and general propositions.   Consider the following analysis of an early episode in Greek political history.

> Why did the Persian expedition come against Athens [in 490 B.C.]? or in other words, what was the cause of her becoming involved in war? Because Athens had . . . raided Sardis [in 497 B.C.]; this was what first started the war.[5]

In this answer Aristotle found both an inductively arrived at universal proposition and a formal principle of deductive inference.   To uncover his reasoning, first let

> C stand for   the Greek city-state "Athens,"
> B denote   "unprovoked aggression," and
> A symbolize   "war."

To make the desired inference he had to show why A must apply as a predicate to C, i.e., why Athens became involved in war.

What did he know?   First, that "B, unprovoked aggression, applies to C, Athens"; secondly, from historical knowledge, he asserted a universal proposition that "A applies to B because war is made upon those who commit an aggressive wrong."   By "A applies to B," he means that "no examples of the subject [B] can be found of which the other term [A] cannot be asserted."   In other words no one who commits wrong (unprovoked) aggression does not become involved in war. With both of these premises, a particular one about Athens' aggression and an inductively arrived at historical law, he claimed that it is possible *logically* to deduce the desired *empirical* conclusion!

To do this, formal models of inference are necessary: "A *syllogism* is a form of words in which, when certain assumptions are made, something other than what has been assumed *necessarily* follows from the fact that the assumptions are such."   Of the more than fifteen logically valid syllogisms, one called *Darii* is particularly relevant to the above example: Let A apply to all B, and B apply to some C; then A must

---

[5] These and succeeding quotations are taken from Aristotle's *The Organum*. Readable translations and very helpful annotations have been provided by Hugh Tredennick in The Loeb Classical Library Series.   For the passages particularly relevant to the present discussion, see *The Organum* (Cambridge, Harvard University Press, 1938 and 1960), Volume I, pp. 184–237, and Volume 2, pp. 2–93 and 207–219.   Italics in all quotations below are mine.

apply to some *C*. The major premise, that *A* applies to all *B*, is asserted as a historical law. The minor premise, that *B* applies to some *C*, here means that some Greek city-state named Athens (in fact there is only one) has committed unprovoked aggression (against Sardis). Therefore, accepting both premises as in fact true allows us logically to infer that "war" (*A*) *must* apply to "Athens" (*C*).[6]

ELEMENTS OF MODERN MATHEMATICS. After having looked at only a few highlights of the mathematics of antiquity (Euclidian geometry and Ptolemaic astronomy have not even been mentioned), with even more rapidity we may touch on several central achievements of modern mathematics. Both the extensive medieval development of Aristotelian logic and the invention of the Arabic number system capable of abstract algebraic manipulations will also not be discussed.

The seventeenth century saw the work of Descartes on analytical geometry and the simultaneous invention of the calculus by Newton and Leibnitz. (The calculus must be used for deducing many of the basic theorems of mathematics, but it has been used only once in this book.)

More recently, mathematicians have concentrated on developing axiomatic treatments—like that of Euclidian geometry—of a wide range of mathematical topics. In the last century, for example, a Russian named Lobachevski found that it was possible to construct a logically consistent geometrical system in which parallel lines *always* meet. The discovery that Euclid's geometry (in which it is an axiom

---

[6] Modern logic studies *propositions* stating *relations* among *predicates* with various subjects rather than general terms joined by various tenses of the verb "to be." Those readers who are curious about how it would symbolize the syllogism used here may consider the following. Let *A*, *B*, and *C* (as used above) be predicates; represent their subjects by variables $x, y, z, \ldots$; together they give abstract clauses or sentences, such as $A(x)$, $B(x)$, or $C(y)$. The first of these, for example, could be read as "*A* is asserted of *x*," or, more simply, "*A* of *x*."

The relation "*A* applies to *B*" is written as a conditional statement: "If *B*, then *A*," symbolically "$B \supset A$." The logical relation "and" is usually denoted by a dot ($\cdot$) and "negation" by a tilde ($\sim$). Universal quantifications of a particular schema or of relations among clauses are introduced by parentheses: $(x)\ (B(x) \supset A(x))$ means, "For all *x*, if $B(x)$, then $A(x)$." The proposition that "Some *A* apply to *C*" is interpretable as an assertion that "there exists a subject *x* which is both *C* and *A*." Using (Ex) for "there exists an *x*," this would be written $(Ex)(C(x) \cdot A(x))$. In its full generality, the syllogism in the text above would then be

$$(x)(B(x) \supset A(x)) \cdot (Ex)(C(x) \cdot B(x)) \supset (Ex)(C(x) \cdot A(x))$$

It provdes a preicise way of symbolizing the statement: "*If* all *B*'s are *A* and there exist some things both *C* and *B*, *then* there exist some things that are both *C* and *A*." For futher examples along these lines the reader is referred to Hughes Leblanc, *An Introduction to Deductive Logic* (New York: Wiley, 1955), Chapter 2.

that parallel lines *never* meet) was not the only logically feasible approach to spatial relations came as a great shock to those who thought mathematics a special kind of knowledge, with empirical (factual) content. The number system of Pythagorean arithmetic was also found to be susceptible to an axiomatic treatment.

When the German mathematician Frege and the British philosophers Bertrand Russell and Alfred North Whitehead proved that all of mathematics could be reduced to the *logical* study of relations among undefined symbols, it became even more certain that mathematics does not *necessarily* convey empirical reality.   Thus a subject that started in the Greek mind as being identical with ultimate reality found itself as purely an intellectual abstraction.   This modern belief, that mathematics has no empirical content, that it consists only of logical tautologies, has in a sense liberated mathematical thought from the necessity of exact correspondence with nature.   Many of its newer disciplines have nonetheless been *applied* to various kinds of natural and social experience.   Chapter 7, for example, illustrates one such twentieth century axiomatic mathematical system: game theory.   For those who doubt the applicability of newer areas of mathematics, it is worth noting that non-Euclidian geometry, which in the nineteenth century so amazed both the mathematical and non-mathematical world, became part of the mathematical model for Einstein's twentieth century theory of relativity.

B.   Early Applications of Mathematics to Politics

Ever since Egyptian geometers measured out the king's lands and apportioned his taxes, mathematics has been applied to the practice and analysis of politics.   Archimedes, for example, who may well have been the first exponent of "operations research," used his geometrical and physical knowledge in the construction of ingenious and deadly war machines.   From a more theoretical point of view, the roles of mathematics in Greek political philosophy and political science are particularly interesting.

MATHEMATICAL DEFINITIONS OF JUSTICE IN CLASSICAL THOUGHT.   It is not surprising that metaphysical beliefs about mathematics are reflected in the key concepts of Greek political theory.   To take but a single example, justice has been given mathematical definitions by Pythagoras, Plato, and Aristotle.

As we have seen, the Pythagoreans felt that underneath everyday experience lay an ultimate numerical reality.   It was thus easy for the

Pythagoreans to derive a numerical principle of justice. Sir Ernest Barker has summarized the argument as follows (recall the spatial representation of the number 9 given above):

> The underlying principle of [the moral] world, it might be argued, was also one of number, or the observance of number. In this way the Pythagoreans came on their conception of justice. Justice was a number. . . : it was a number multiplied into itself, a square number. A square number is a perfect harmony, because it is composed of equal parts, and the number of the parts is equal to the numerical value of each part. . . . [It] follows that justice is based on the conception of a State composed of equal parts. A number is square so long as the equality of its parts remains: a State is just, so long as it is distinguished by the equality of its parts. Justice is the preservation of such equality.[7]

A convincing case can be made that "the Platonic world of ideas [or forms] is the refined, revised form of the Pythagorean doctrine that number lies at the base of the real world."[8] We might therefore expect Plato's definitions of justice, the highest ideal for the individual, as well as the state, to be mathematical in nature. Barker, for example, cites a passage in *Gorgias* referring to the idea of geometrical equality. In the *Republic*, Plato introduces a proportional, allegorical definition drawing on Pythagoras' musical discoveries: by self-mastery, "the just man" brings into a "well-tempered harmony" the three parts of his soul—reason, appetite and spirit—"like the terms in the proportion of a musical scale, the highest and lowest notes and the mean between them, with all the intermediate intervals."[9]

For Aristotle, like Plato, the mathematical sciences were concerned with general forms; they did not confine themselves to particulars. By the time of his greatest mathematical contributions, however, Aristotle did not accept the Platonic view that forms exist apart from the particular things they embodied. As we have seen, he was able to

[7] Ernest Barker, *The Political Thought of Plato and Aristotle* (New York: Dover, 1959), pp. 19–20.

[8] A. N. Whitehead, *Science and the Modern World* (A Mentor Book; New York: The New American Library, 1959), p. 33. Sarton, *op. cit.*, p. 432, comes to the same conclusion, but with rather different overtones: ". . . we may safely assume that the Platonic theory of Ideas had a mathematical origin, and take its formulation as one proof among others of Plato's immoderate and irrational mathematization of everything." Accepting the central influence of Pythagorean numerology on Plato's theory of Ideas does not imply that Plato was unable to distinguish between mathematical objects and ultimate Ideas. In his *Republic*, Plato's educational program for guardians required five years study in "Dialectics" *after* ten years of mathematics.

[9] *The Republic of Plato*, translated with an Introduction and notes by Francis Cornford (New York: Oxford University Press, 1956), p. 142. See also pp. 175–193 and 221–263.

distinguish propositions of universal validity abstracted from history from syllogisms empty of any particular content. We would therefore expect him to be more aware of the difficulties of applying his "proportionate equality" definition of justice to a particular situation:

> All men agree that just distributions consist in distribution according to merit; but all men do not mean the same thing when they speak of merit. Democrats mean free birth; oligarchs mean wealth, or sometimes good birth; aristocrats mean goodness.[10]

In these quotations justice has been given geometric, arithmetic, and, by analogy, musical definitions, all derived from the basic Greek area of scholarship known as mathematics. They center on the notions of equality and proportion. Regardless of the tenability of their various metaphysical presuppositions, Greek philosophers did make an important contribution in suggesting the relevance of mathematics to the study of political ideals. As we shall see in Chapter 3, their ideas of justice and inequality can be generalized and applied to a wide range of political situations.

ARISTOTELIAN POLITICAL SCIENCE. Scientifically, Aristotle's interests extended beyond those of either Pythagoras or Plato: he participated in the classification and analysis of everything from sentence predicates and biological specimens to political constitutions. As we shall see in Chapter 2, his ideas were quite sophisticated in terms of recent mathematical theories of measurement. For example, he *classified* constitutions in terms of the presence or absence of the attribute of "rightness" (rule in the common interest); then he *ordered* or arranged rightful and unjust constitutions according to the degree of their rightness. When in the common interest, he held that government by the one was superior to government by the few, which in turn surpassed unselfish government by the many; for self-interested governments, just the opposite ordering was established. By using an unusual kind of measurement, Aristotle was additionally able to locate actual constitutions as closer to one or another of two unequally "perverted" forms of government: among constitutions that are mixtures of selfish government by the few ("oligarchy") and by the many ("democracy"), he labeled those mixtures "which incline to democracy" as "polities" and "those which incline more to oligarchy" as "aristocracies."[11]

Aristotle and his students collected detailed information on the constituent principles of more than 150 political communities. Proceeding

---

[10] *Ethics*, Book V, c. III, ¶7. Quoted in Ernest Barker, *The Politics of Aristotle* (New York: Oxford University Press, 1958), pp. 20 and 364.

[11] *The Politics of Aristotle, op. cit.*, pp. 110–116, 154–159.

inductively from these masses of data, Aristotle further refined the above classifications and offered numerous propositions about the kinds of constitutions most appropriate for a variety of specific social and economic circumstances and about the causes of revolutions and political stability.[12]   Similar analyses of cross-national political data and the degree to which variables like economic circumstances are associated with revolutionary violence are contained in Chapters 4 and 5 of this book.   One further question closely related to Aristotle's concern with syllogistic reasoning, the meaning of causality in such statistical comparisons, is also discussed in Chapter 6.[13]

C.   Mathematics for Political Analysis

Although this review has only touched on some of the more important ideas and political applications of mathematics, perhaps it will suffice to suggest its constituent elements.   Taken together, they may be considered a descriptive definition of the field of particular relevance for those contemplating mathematical political analysis.

1.   *Mathematics studies formal, content-free relationships.*   In place of the Platonic view that ideal forms underlie all earthly experience, modern mathematics has substituted the view that the formulas of mathematics are abstract and content-free relationships.   Whatever

[12] *Ibid.*, pp. 79–86, 203–278.

[13] Interest in the classification, measurement, and association of state characteristics reappeared in the middle of the seventeenth century.   The story has been well told by Paul Lazarsfeld, "Notes on the History of Quantification in Sociology—Trends, Sources and Problems" in Harry Woolf, *Quantification: A History of the Meaning of Measurement in the Natural and Social Sciences* (Indianapolis: Bobbs-Merrill, 1961), pp. 147–203.   Defining quantification in the social sciences to include "mere counting, the development of classificatory dimensions and the systematic use of social symptoms as well as mathematical models and an axiomatic theory of measurement" (p. 147), Lazarsfeld describes two roots of modern statistics (a term derived from the Latin word for state).   "Political arithmetic" was developed, among others, by William Petty, whose *Political Anatomy of Ireland* (1672) studied the relation between the social structure of the country and the chances of its good government in a newly independent country.   The German root, called "university statistics," developed from the work of Hermann Conring, who classified knowledge about states under an Aristotelian rubric of final, formal, material, and efficient causation.   These traditions came from two different backgrounds: "The Englishman, citizen of an empire, looked for causal relations between quantitative variables. The German, subject to one of 300 small principalities and . . . involved in the petty policies of many of them, tried to derive systematically the best set of categories by which a state could be characterized" (p. 155).   When adequate data became available, in the German nationalistic flowering of the late eighteenth century, the German school developed a similar concern with quantitative causal questions. These ideas are usually considered the foundations of modern statistical analysis.

empirical meaning mathematical statements have is due entirely to the interpretations which are given to these formulas and to the assumptions from which the formulas are derived. In this sense, correctly deduced but uninterpreted mathematical statements are neither true nor false; their *applications* to particular realms of experience, however, are legitimate subjects of debate. In modern terminology, mathematics *per se* is logical, not empirical, analysis.

2. *Mathematical statements may be qualitative, quantitative, or both.* In Pythagorean terms, the discrete and the continuous formed the primary branches of mathematical knowledge. In the syllogism used above, for example, the premises and conclusions are quantitative specifications of the frequency of occurrence of abstract predicates, which, in turn, were qualitatively interpreted as "being Athens," "committing aggression," and so forth. Even though the "rightness" of particular kinds of constitutions sounds like a qualitative attribute referring to the *degree* of their "rightness" and describing inclinations within these orderings both imply quantitative assessment. When Aristotle associates the attribute "rightness" with the size of the sovereign body (the one, the few, or the many), he is at the same time performing both qualitative and quantitative analysis.

These examples illustrate an important point: arguments about the applicability of mathematics to politics need not forever be phrased in terms of the "quantitative" versus "non-quantitative" approach. More germane questions ask about the kinds of measurement appropriate to sets of data which, if meaningful, can at least be categorized. Also more to the point is the value in a particular field of an explicit, formal, logical analysis. Some mathematically oriented political scientists have admitted that formal models, whatever individual interpretation they are given, do not have nearly the richness in semantic content as similar statements in ordinary English. Their case for mathematical models is that, using the appropriate methods, they have a more unambiguous extractable content than do most verbal theories.[14]

3. *The elements of mathematical reasoning are numerical, spatial, or symbolic.* In one sense, this statement follows from our earlier remark about "qualitative" mathematics—qualities may be attributes, spatial relations, or logical symbols. From a related point of view, all three of these properties of mathematical objects are fused in the early Greek representation of numbers: as patterns of dots in the sand. We have

[14] Herbert Simon and Allen Newell, "Models: Their Uses and Limitations," in Leonard D. White (ed.), *The State of the Social Sciences* (Chicago: University of Chicago Press, 1956), pp. 66–83.

also seen that modern geometry and logic are primarily concerned with spatial, numerical, and logical relationships.

Nonetheless, a common misperception is that mathematics always requires the use of numbers;[15] in political analysis the same opinion, that mathematics is only appropriate to data which have been precisely measured, is often heard. The measures of attribute association reviewed in Chapter 4 suggest appropriate alternatives to such a view.

4. *In addition to deduction, mathematicians are often concerned with the logic of inductive inference and measurement.* We have already mentioned two examples of early mathematical reasoning using a deductive method. Pythagorean geometry derived its conclusions from a small set of undefined concepts and postulates. In showing that $\sqrt{2}$ is an irrational number, it used the method of "proof by contradiction." If irrationals did not exist, odd numbers could be shown to be even; therefore irrationals had to exist. Logical deductions from premises to conclusions and their relation to causal knowledge and scientific universals were first placed on a systematic basis in Aristotle's *Organum.* The power of his syllogisms resulted from their applicability to different subjects. Bertrand Russell has emphasized the relationship between the power of mathematical deductions and the "emptiness" of their conclusions: "If our hypothesis is about *anything* and not about some one or more particular things, then our deductions constitute mathematics.[16]

Although instructive Russell's quotation is misleading to the extent that it obscures the role of deductive mathematics in the *inductive* procedures of measurement and generalization of major concern to statistically inclined political analysts. The method of Guttman scaling to be discussed in Chapter 2, would be a simple example of such a concern, but we need not limit the argument to modern instances.

The writings of Pythagoras, Plato, and Aristotle all contain measurements and generalizations. Either directly or by analogy, each thinker developed qualitative classifications or quantitative standards against

[15] John Kemeny has tried to correct this misperception in a provocatively titled article: "Mathematics Without Numbers," *Daedalus*, **88**, 4 (Fall 1959), pp. 577–591. His examples are from graph theory (a derivative of geometry), algebraic group theory, the matrix analysis of communication networks, and a logical approach to the study of Arrow's impossibility theorem and the "Voters' Paradox," both of which are discussed in Chapter 7. The entire *Daedalus* issue, edited by Daniel Lerner and entitled *Quantity and Quality*, is of special relevance to problems of social science quantification.

[16] Bertand Russell, quoted by Philip Jourdain, "The Nature of Mathematics," in James R. Newman, *The World of Mathematics* (New York: Simon and Schuster, 1956), p. 4.

which to compare the characteristics of music, justice, or of geometrical figures. Measuring the effective length of the monochord, for example, helped Pythagoras generalize his findings to universal laws of music; the incommensurability of the diagonal of a square led him into the discovery of irrational numbers. Plato, like Aristotle, ordered various constitutions as to their distance from an ideal. In fact, he is given credit for synthesizing the rational and irrational numbers into one continuum, in effect allowing measurements using any of the "real numbers" above zero. We have already seen how Aristotle's political classifications and data collection schemes allowed him to make historical inferences of some generality from which, syllogistically, other interpretations could be deduced. In each of these cases, both inductive and deductive logical reasoning were involved.

SUMMARY. In summarizing these observations, we may say that *mathematics is the logical study of symbolic relationships.* The formal, content-free symbols may be qualitative or quantitative—numbers, spatial relations, or abstract sentence predicates. Logically, mathematical relationships can represent both deductive and inductive inferences. Measurements are logically consistent steps toward inductive generalizations; sometimes measurable characteristics of political phenomena can logically be deduced from higher generalizations.

CHAPTER 2

Politics and Its Measurement

> *Measurement is the business of pinning numbers on things*
> S. S. STEVENS

MATHEMATICS STUDIES SYSTEMS of logical interrelationships among qualitative and quantitative symbols. Because by their nature they are free of any specific substantive content, these abstract logical systems have been applied to a wide range of human experience, including politics. The first step in any such application is a measurement problem: to determine what kind of mathematics, if it exists, is suitable for the phenomena being studied and for the methods of analysis being used. Before taking up the general problem of measuring politics with the appropriate kind of mathematics, it will therefore be helpful to review some of the ways in which politics has been defined and studied.

A. Definitions of Politics

The relationship between politics and the intellectual discipline that studies it, here referred to as political analysis, can cause considerable confusion. The word "politics" itself can refer either to facts or to scholarship. Certainly these meanings are closely related because findings about the object of study are influenced by the kinds of questions that are asked and the methods used for ascertaining the answers. Nonetheless, for expository purposes, we shall try verbally to separate several definitions of politics from the methods proposed for its study.

THE ARISTOTELIAN VIEW. The fundamental unit of early Greek political thought was their paramount form of political community, the city-state. The nature of the *polis*, as it was called, was described by its *politea*, its constitution. Aristotle defined a constitution as "an organization of offices in a state, by which the method of their distribution is fixed, the sovereign authority is determined, and the nature of the ends to be pursued by the association and all its members is pre-

13

scribed."[1]   Although there are problems of translating Greek concepts into an English vocabulary, it is clear that Aristotle included in his view of "politics" the institutional patterns and practices of governments. He also paid particular attention to the ways in which officials were selected and the goals or interests that they pursued.

SEVERAL MODERN VIEWS.   Modern political analysts have continued to refer to the distribution of authority and power in the institutions of government and to the goals or interests they serve.   More emphasis, however, has been directed toward objective descriptions of the political behavior of various individuals within different kinds of political associations.

Max Weber, an important German social scientist, has called any association "political" "in so far as the enforcement of its order is carried out continually within a given territorial area by the application and threat of physical force on the part of the administrative staff."[2] Weber's view relates Aristotle's "sovereign authority" to its territorial limits and focuses, as objectively as possible, on the bureaucratic institutions of the modern state and on their political leadership.   He brings clearly into the open the importance of legitimate force that states may employ in obtaining their ends.

Two political scientists, Robert A. Dahl and David Easton, have offered definitions of politics which illustrate slightly different modern viewpoints.   By drawing explicitly from the work of Aristotle, Weber, Parsons, and others, Dahl has defined political systems as "any persistent pattern of human relationships that involves, to a significant extent, power, rule, or authority," all relationships in which individuals are somehow induced to do things that they otherwise would not do.   Empirically, Dahl criticizes the idealized Aristotelian notion of the self-sufficiency of the city-state, culturally, economically, or militarily, as a means for pursuing the good life.   His definition of political relationships thus makes very clear the possibility that "politics" exists in patterns of behavior that are not coextensive with national societies.   International business firms and intranational religious organizations can be considered as political associations.   Dahl does

[1] Ernest Barker, *The Politics of Aristotle* (New York: Oxford University Press, 1958), pp. 154–156.

[2] Max Weber, *The Theory of Social and Economic Organization*, translated by A. M. Henderson and Talcott Parsons (New York: Oxford University Press, 1947), p. 154; quoted in Robert A. Dahl's excellent and readable introduction, *Modern Political Analysis* (Englewood Cliffs, N.J.: Prentice-Hall, 1963), p. 5.

follow Aristotle, however, in defining and observing "offices" or "roles" in stable and complex political systems.[3]

Consciously aware of the methodological implications of his "convenient guide" for political analysis, David Easton defines politics as "the authoritative allocation of values for a society."[4] By authoritative allocation Easton means what we usually think of as decisions promulgated by executive, legislative, and judicial office-holders. Describing the characteristic *function* of these officials, allocating valued goods and services, rather than their institutional *location*, allows him to talk about the politics of primitive societies, where a set of formalized political offices do not exist. In allocation or policy-making processes, the characteristic result is that some things are authoritatively denied to some people and made accessible to others.

By emphasizing *authoritative* allocations for an *entire* society, Easton is trying to limit the rather broad notion of politics used by Dahl and others, excluding smaller or larger units such as business and churches, as long as their decisions are not felt to be authoritative by the members of the society as a whole. In contrast with Aristotle's and Dahl's definitions, Easton focuses on *both* the goals of policy-makers seeking to alter the distribution of values in a society, and the authority or power relationships involved. This difference between attention to policy processes and to policy outcomes reappears in the writings of most political scientists and philosophers.

In defining politics, Harold Lasswell has adopted the "working attitude of practicing politicians."[5] Practical politicians are concerned with getting and distributing the rewards and penalties of politics: values such as influence, power, prestige, wealth, and security. Influence means current or potential value position; it may or may not be exercised in actual political decisions. The influential are those who obtain the greater part of available particular values. Membership in the influential elite may be extremely restricted or more widely dispersed, depending on how widely values are shared and how restrictively the

[3] Dahl, *op. cit.*, Chapter 2.

[4] David Easton, *The Political System* (New York: Knopf, 1953), Chapter 5.

[5] This review of Lasswell's ideas on the nature of politics, and his set of questions for political analysis discussed below, are derived from his *Politics: Who Gets What, When, How*, which has been reprinted together with a Postscript (1958) (Cleveland: World Publishing Company, 1958); H. D. Lasswell and A. Kaplan, *Power and Society, A Framework for Political Inquiry* (New Haven: Yale University Press, 1950); and H. D. Lasswell, *The Future of Political Science* (New York: Atherton Press, 1963).

elite is defined. In one sense, then, politics is defined by politicians who ask, "Who gets what, when, how?"

More generally, Lasswell has also described politics as the "shaping and sharing of power," referring to both the policy process and its outcomes. Power is conceived to be a special kind of influence, in which severe deprivations or sanctions are threatened in the case of noncompliance with preferred policies in social relationships. Presumably, large rewards are also used to induce policy compliance. This view generalizes Weber's notion of physical sanctions to severe deprivations of any value—wealth, power, health, or respect—and it stresses the value allocation process and its payoffs in a manner similar to Easton's approach.

For Lasswell, authority is formalized, subjectively legitimate power. Thus his conception of political process contains both authoritative relationships (as studied by Easton) and more naked power (as studied by Weber and by Dahl). The relevant arenas, however, include whole societies, other stable social relationships (also studied by Dahl), and even largely unstructured but potentially deprivational situations. Lasswell has, however, increasingly focused on the national and international context:

> I have, I trust, made it plain that the fundamental facts of politics are inextricable from human society, if by politics we mean the largest arena of interaction in which goals are clarified, degrees of achievement are described, conditioning factors are analyzed, future developments are projected and policy alternatives are invented and evaluated.[6]

B.   Questions Asked by Political Analysis

Lasswell's statement brings us from definitions of politics to the description of the main tasks of political analysis. His approach is to reconstruct the kinds of questions practical politicians as value allocators must deal with explicitly or implicitly. These include both empirical and normative questions. Comparing Lasswell's list with those of other commentators reveals a remarkable degree of overlapping.

1. *What goal values (preferred events) are to be sought?* This question is the traditional concern of political philosophy in its quest for the meaning and purpose of the political community. Aristotle wanted to know what was the ideally best constitution for a *polis*, as well as the relatively best and most enduring constitution for citizens with different psychological and socio-economic characteristics. Easton and Dahl

[6] *The Future of Political Science, op. cit.*, p. 241.

are both interested in research on criteria for evaluating the moral worth of different policies. The important point is the wide agreement among political analysts on the need to clarify community goals.

2. *What are the historical trends in the accumulation and enjoyment of values?* Describing historical trends up through current developments takes a great deal of time and skill. First, there is the problem of collecting all, or at least a judicious sample, of the relevant evidence. Even in modern times, evidence about some states is very hard to get: both Russia and the United States send satellites hundreds of miles into the sky for that very purpose!

Just as important as getting the evidence is the ability to make some sense from it. It required Toynbee to frame the phrase "the revolution of rising expectations." In testing the validity of this generalization, both Toynbee and his readers must have specific ways of saying what his concepts mean. Has such a revolution occurred in both the cities and the rural villages of the underdeveloped world? Which expectations have undergone what kind of revolution? The same kinds of questions have to be asked of another politically relevant (and more controversial) generalization: that the appeal of Communism has increased for the underdeveloped countries. As this chapter indicates relevant value and accurate historical generalizations require both sophisticated concepts and concrete ways of seeing when they apply.

3. *What factors condition or explain actual historical developments?* The main task of political science and empirical political theory is accurately and objectively to explain political processes and their value outcomes. When it is possible to obtain repeated observations at one time or in subsequent periods about related phenomena, some kind of explanation is usually possible. Aristotle's theory of constitutions suggests, for example, that states with larger middle classes will enjoy greater stability. Historically, he developed his theory with reference to Greek city-states, but it is still at least plausible for the nation states of today.

Such explanations are not entirely satisfactory, however, until the analyst is assured that other possible explanations do not apply. The skeptic could suggest that only high levels of economic development, not large middle classes, will bring about stable governments. The question of what constitutes a more adequate explanation is discussed at some length in Chapters 4, 5, and 6 below.

4. *What projections characterize the probable course of future developments?* Politicians and policy-makers must be concerned with probable future developments; skilled political analysts have a major

responsibility to "re-edit the maps of the future, and to improve the methods by which the job is done." Some of Lasswell's most imaginative work has been directed toward better understanding of future contingencies, such as the development of "garrison states" like those portrayed in Orwell's *1984*, revolutionary possibilities for the use of natural energy resources, and the effects of man's control of his own genetic evolution.[7] Making useful predictions about the future, even when it is hoped that policies will be found that will prevent such predictions from coming true requires both scientific knowledge and responsible imagination.

5. *What policy alternatives will bring the greatest net realization of values?* Aristotle asked about the best kind of government for given sets of conditions. Taken in a less comprehensive manner, this question refers to preferable policies that a political association should follow. The invention and evaluation of policy alternatives have been crucial steps in the careers of all politicians. Moral philosophers, sociologists, and welfare economists have also had to evaluate social policies. Several ways in which mathematical analyses can contribute to goal clarification and policy evaluation are discussed in Chapters 3 and 7.

Taken together, these questions include the main ways in which politics has been analyzed. The tasks involved include the conceptualization of the phenomena being considered, their objective description and explanation, and the evaluation of various policy alternatives for maximizing the goals of a political association.

C.   Qualitative and Quantitative Political Analysis

In analyzing politics it is possible to compare properties of both individuals and groups. We talk about the wealth and power of a nation and the personality and attitudes of a government official. But before we can explain one of these variable characteristics by using another, we need a carefully specified way of measuring them. Knowledge about the various kinds of measurement and their applicability greatly improves any mathematical analysis of politics.

---

[7] In particular, see his "The Garrison State," *American Journal of Sociology*, **XLVI** (Jan., 1941), pp. 455–468, and his Presidential address to the American Political Science Association, "The Political Science of Science," *American Political Science Review*, **50** (December 1956), pp. 961–979.

Although many of the analyses in subsequent chapters will imply certain trends or projections, two relevant mathematical disciplines, economic time series analysis and computer simulation projection techniques, are both beyond the scope of this book. Appropriate readings are discussed in Lasswell's *The Future of Political Science*.

QUALITATIVE MEASUREMENT. S. S. Stevens has called measurement "the business of pinning numbers on things."[8] Although delightfully simple, this quote is at first a little confusing. Some things, like a person's religion, or the country from which he comes, do not seem to be susceptible to meaningful numerical labels. In this puzzling situation Stevens suggests that numbers *can* be used for qualitative measurements, i.e., in the same way that numbers are used to identify football players! The main purpose served by athletes' numbers is to distinguish each of them from his fellow team members. (Three different quarterbacks all with the number 13 on their backs are not allowed.)

In more formalized language, any set of categories that is mutually exhaustive (include all cases) and exclusive (with no case in more than one category) can be called a *nominal scale*. Numbers or verbal labels (like Catholic, Jew, or Protestant) serve as labels or names for distinct categories. An acceptable nominal scale measurement of Senatorial religion would not be very difficult to find; however, much harder problems of nominal scale political measurement exist, e.g., which organizations are "extremist" and which are not? Classifying nations as to whether or not they are "democracies" is really hard to do without carefully worded instructions as to democracy's definitional characteristics.

Mathematically, the basic property of this simplest kind of measurement is that things belonging in one category are equal to each other but not to anything else in their identical aspect. After some thought, mathematicians have come to agree on the logical properties characteristic of the equals relationship (symbolized by "$=$"). By using the letters a, b, and c as abstract symbols that could be interpreted in a variety of ways, they are:

1. Reflexivity: $a = a$
   (Anything is equal to itself.)

[8] Some of the pioneering work on the meaning of measurement in the social sciences has been done by S. S. Stevens, Clyde H. Coombs, and Paul Lazarsfeld. See, for example, S. S. Stevens, "Measurement, Psychophysics and Utility," in C. West Churchman and Philburn Ratoosh, *Measurement: Definitions and Theories* (New York: Wiley, 1959), pp. 18–63; C. H. Coombs, "Theory and Methods of Social Measurement," in Leon Festinger and Daniel Katz, eds., *Research Methods in the Behavioral Sciences* (New York: Dryden Press, 1953), pp. 471–535; and Paul F. Lazarsfeld and Allen H. Barton, "Qualitative Measurement in the Social Sciences: Classification, Typologies and Indices," in Daniel Lerner and Harold D. Lasswell, *The Policy Sciences: Recent Developments in Scope and Method* (Stanford, Calif.: Stanford University Press, 1951), pp. 155–192. Much of the recent economic literature on measurement is unfortunately beyond the scope of the beginning student.

2. Symmetry: If $a = b$, then $b = a$
(Things on either side of an equals sign both equal each other.)

3. Transitivity: If $a = b$ and $b = c$, then $a = c$
(Things both equal to something else equal each other.)

Reflexive, symmetric, and transitive relationships will always hold for members *within* categories but not necessarily *between* categories of a nominal scale. Thus all Senators are at least nominally of the Protestant, Catholic, or Jewish faith. The relation "has the same religion as" will separate all Senators into mutually exclusive and collectively exhaustive groups.

One further mathematical distinction about nominal scales has to do with the number of categories in the scale. A Senator's religion was considered above to be a trichotomous, qualitative attribute. It would have been easier, perhaps, to *dichotomize* religion into a twofold distinction: Protestant or non-Protestant.

Pinning numbers on athletes after a race is over makes additional sense. We can rank them as first, second, third, and so on. At the end of a relay race (or a football season) we can similarly say that members of one team "were on a faster team than" those of another. An *ordinal scale* of measurement allows one to make "more or less" statements about exclusive and exhaustive categories that already form a nominal scale.

There are several extremely interesting ways in which political phenomena can be ordinally scaled. Many trends and comparisons of value distributions are stated in this way. The President is more poweful than members of Congress, who in turn are more powerful than most other citizens. Economists may order their preferences regarding two or more ways of financing medical care. Supreme Court justices are often ordered as to how "liberal" they are. In Chapter 7 we shall see how difficult it is to find a rational way of ordering *collective* policy preferences.

Mathematically, there are several ways of symbolizing an ordinal relationship. The most frequently used symbols "$<$" and "$>$" are interpreted as "is less than" or as "is greater than." Sometimes it is also convenient to combine the statements "a is less than b" and "a is equal to b" to read "a is less than or equal to b," denoted by "$a \leq b$." The expression "$a \geq b$" has a parallel interpretation.

By using these notational conveniences it is possible formally to characterize the properties of an ordinal relationship among groups or individuals. Like the ordinal numbers (1st, 2nd, 3rd, etc.), ordinal categories are irreflexively, antisymmetrically, and transitively related. Symbolically, these properties can be stated as follows:

1. Irreflexivity: a is not $> a$.
   (Note that $\geqq$ is reflexive, however, because $a \geqq a$.)
2. Antisymmetry: If $a > b$, then b is not $> a$.
3. Transitivity: If $a > b$ and $b > c$, then $a > c$.

The reader may like to construct ordinal classifications of Senators or nations according to their levels of power. Being sure that all three of the above characteristics of an ordinal relationship are satisfied is not as easy as it looks, especially if objects are compared only two at a time.

QUANTITATIVE MEASUREMENT. Nominal and ordinal scales are usually considered examples of qualitative measurement, even though ordinal relationships do talk about questions of degree and have some interesting mathematical properties. We can say qualitatively that one nation is wealthier or more powerful than another, or that President Eisenhower was "more liberal than" Senator Taft on foreign affairs. The essential characteristic of quantitative kinds of measurement is that they go on to ask "how much more?"[9]

Trying quantitatively to measure political phenomena, like differences or changes in the distribution of wealth and power, is challenging and difficult, but the theoretical and practical benefits are significant. Sometimes economic indicators can be used—the average per capita income in United States dollar equivalents of different countries is one indicator of national wealth, just as total gross national products indicate at least one kind of potential power in international politics. The total power of different international coalitions, for example, could not be measured unless individual nations' power potentials are quantitatively defined.

Attitudes and preferences are also sometimes quantitatively measured. Let us consider the problem of trying to say how much more liberal one official is than another. Indices of Senatorial "liberalism" have been constructed by *adding* the number of times a Senator has

---

[9] Recall that after ordering several kinds of constitutions as to their "rightness," Aristotle then tried to say which differences between ranks were bigger than others. Coombs would call this kind of quantitative measurement an "ordered-metric" scale.

supported legislation considered to have a liberal versus conservative component.[10] This approach results in units of measurement ("pro-liberal" votes and "antiliberal" votes) which are assumed to be of equal weight.

Mathematically, characterizing a particular property with a fixed unit of measurement means measuring it with an *interval scale*. When the numbers 5, 8, and 10 are pinned on three different Senators (call them *A*, *B*, *C*) as measures of their liberalism, it is assumed not only that those with higher scores are *more* liberal, but also that Senator B is 3 units and that Senator C is 5 units more liberal than Senator A. Interval levels of measurement tell us about *differences* between individuals and groups; they can meaningfully be added and subtracted. (Adding and subtracting nominal scales is like adding and subtracting football players' identification numbers, and is *not* very meaningful.)

An even higher form of measurement is possible. Considering again the same approach to measuring Senatorial liberalism (about which more will be said below), it would be very nice to know, but very difficult to find out, just how many "yes" votes should be considered to indicate the *absence* of liberalism. Votes indicating only weak support are not often included in liberalism scales. For this reason adding or subtracting any fixed number of points to an interval scale does not change the amount of information it contains. Scores of 0, 3, and 5, for example, still show the correct amount of intervals between the three Senators as do 5, 8, and 10. Even multiplying interval scores by a fixed positive number does not change their basic relationships. Scores of 0.0, 0.3, and 0.5 would still show Senators B and C in the same relation to Senator A. Only the unit of comparison has changed its magnitude from 1.0 to 0.1.

Now if we could say that a score of zero really means a complete lack of liberalism, we would know from the first scores given above (5, 8, 10) that Senator C was 2 *times* as liberal as Senator A, while Senator B was four-fifths as liberal as Senator C. Interval measurement scales like this one, with *non-arbitrary zero points*, are known as *ratio scales*. They are always interval scales; they can be added and subtracted. But as we have just seen, ratio scales can also meaningfully be multiplied and divided.

Several additional mathematical properties of ratio scales are worth noting. Let us say that Senators A and B have liberalism scores of 3 and 6, respectively. Multiplying or dividing these numbers by positive num-

---

[10] Both the Americans for Democratic Action (a liberal group) and the Americans for Constitutional Action (a conservative group) have developed these kinds of scales, often expressed in terms of percentages.

bers does not change their distinctive numerical relationship: 6 is twice as big as 3; 2 times 6 is twice as big as 2 times 3, etc. Symbolically,

$$\frac{6}{3} = \frac{2 \cdot 6}{2 \cdot 3} = \frac{\frac{1}{2} \cdot 6}{\frac{1}{2} \cdot 3} = \frac{2}{1}$$

The basic mathematical characteristic of two measurements on any ratio scale is that the ratio of the two scores remains the same. In the above equations this ratio is 2 to 1.

Unlike interval scales, however, adding or subtracting numbers from ratio scores does change their value. Take 2 away from 6 and 3, for example, gives a very different ratio of 4 to 1 for liberalism scores. One Senator cannot at the same time be both twice as liberal and four times as liberal as another.

D. Requirements of Scientific Descriptions

Nominal, ordinal, interval, and ratio scales have been presented as various ways of pinning numbers, or other symbols, on political things. Each kind (or "level") of measurement was found to contain the properties of the earlier kinds. Thus, for example, all ratio scales have ordinal properties, while all interval scales include nominal characteristics. It is easy to show that the requirements for these four kinds of measurement themselves obey the irreflexive, antisymmetric, and transitive requirements of an ordinal scale! This result is helpful to those trying to quantify political characteristics because if the mathematical requirements of one level of measurement do not apply, it is often possible to reduce by one or two ranks the level of measurement being used.

The rule that properties of objects correspond to those of the mathematics by which they are measured is one general requirement of scientific descriptions. It is possible to summarize a more inclusive list of these requirements, some of which have already been briefly alluded to, as operationally definable concepts and relationships, reliable measurements, and subjective and objective validity.

OPERATIONAL DEFINITIONS. Theoretical concepts like liberalism, democracy, and the revolution of rising expectations all require operational definitions before their properties can scientifically be described and compared.

To illustrate one way in which such varying characteristics can be operationally defined, we shall describe a technique known as Guttman scaling. As applied by Glendon Schubert to assess Supreme Court opinions on questions of economic liberalism (in matters such as labor-management relations, monopoly problems, etc.), this technique can generate an ordinal classification of judicial attitudes.   In Table 2.1 nine justices are ranked as to the degree of their economic liberalism on the basis of twenty-five different cases they all decided.   The more liberal justices are in the top rows of the table, and the cases evoking the most liberal responses are on the right.

Guttman scaling is a more exacting way of operationalizing liberalism than the "number of pro-liberal votes" approach discussed above. Working from a preliminary set of decisions that are thought to involve the same substantive content, it uses as indicators of a particular attitude only those decisions that can be shown to lie along a single, unidimensional continuum.   The problem that the number of "pro-liberal votes" may not indicate the most liberal judge is therefore largely avoided.   *If* issues can be arranged so that, knowing a justice's most liberal opinion allows us to predict all his other positions on more conservative or more radical alternatives, a single, clearly defined attitude continuum can be constructed.

The ordering of issues in Table 2.1 shows that only 13 out of 213 votes could not have been predicted by knowing a justice's most consistent, pro-liberal position.   In the table votes inconsistent with the issue ordering are indicated by minus signs.   Note also the close (but imperfect) relationships between the overall liberalism ranks and the total votes "For" and "Against" in the last three columns of the table.

The above paragraphs briefly describe and apply an operational definition of judicial economic liberalism.   Other studies have also shown that several specific aspects of "liberalism" can be meaningfully defined by using the Guttman scaling technique.   Duncan MacRae, for example,[11] found distinct scales of legislative internationalism, economic liberalism, and support for civil liberties.

MEASUREMENT RELIABILITY.   The general procedure outlined above is not yet sufficient to let us decide whether or not a given scale can be said to be satisfactorily defined.   One point remaining has to do with the degree of reliability, i.e., reproducibility, of the scaling procedure.[12]

---

[11] Duncan MacRae, Jr., *Dimensions of Congressional Voting* (Berkeley: University of California Press, 1958).

[12] Besides a high enough level of reproducibility, Guttman also required, in his original description of scalability, that items with a wide range of marginal distributions of responses be included, especially those with nearly equal numbers of positive and negative replies; that errors be randomly distributed; that, if possible, the number of items be greater than 10; and that the greatest possible number of response categories be used. See Samuel A. Stouffer, Louis Guttman *et al.*, *Measurement and Prediction* (Princeton: Princeton University Press, 1950), especially Chapter 3, "The Basis of Scalogram Analysis."

Cases

Justices	1	2	3	4	5	6	7	8	9	10	11	12	13	14	15	16	17	18	19	20	21	22	23	24	25	Total "For"	Votes "Against"	Rank
Douglas	+	+	+	+	+	+	+	-	+	-	+	+	+	+	+	+	+	+	+	+	+	+	+	+	+	23	2	1
Black	+	+	+	+	+	+	+	+	+	+	+	+	+	+	+	+	+	+	+	+	+	+	+	+		24	1	2
Warren	+	+	+	+	+	+	+	+	+	+	+	+	+	+	+	+	+	+								18	7	3.5
Brennan	-	+	+	+	+	+	+	+	+	+	+	+	+	+	+	+	+	+								17	8	3.5
Clark	+	+	-	-	-	-	+	+	+	+	a	+	+	+	+	+										11	13	5
Harlan	+	+	+	+	+	+	-	+	+	+	a															9	15	6
Stewart	-	+	+	+	+	+	+	a																		6	18	7
Frankfurter	+	a	a	a	a	a	a								±	a	a						a			2	14	8
Whittaker												±	±	±												3	22	9
Total Votes For/Against	6/3	7/1	6/2	6/2	6/2	6/2	6/2	5/3	6/3	5/4	4/3	6/3	6/3	6/3	6/3	5/3	4/4	4/5	2/7	2/7	2/7	2/7	2/6	2/7	1/8	113/	100	

* Adopted with permission from Glendon Schubert, The 1960 Term: A Psychological Analysis, American Political Science Review, LVI, No. 1 (March, 1962), p. 100. Consistent pro-Liberalism votes are denoted by a +, consistent opposition by a blank. Inconsistent pro- and con-votes are labelled ± and -. The a's signify absence or non-participation. Cases are identified in the original article.

Table 2.1. An ordinal classification of supreme court attitudes toward economic liberalism, 1960 term.*

Operational procedures should usually give the same results. The problem of the reproducibility of a Guttman scale can be studied in several ways. Perhaps one could take different halves of the set of decisions being ranked and see how close the rankings of justices corresponded in the two different sets of decisions. Another approach to the reliability problem is to define a Coefficient of Reproducibility (C.R.) and choose an arbitrary level of acceptability for it. For an ordering of cases so that the number of out-of-order or "inconsistent" responses is reduced to a minimum, Guttman defined a

$$\text{Coefficient of Reproducibility as } 1 - \frac{\text{inconsistent responses}}{\text{total responses}}$$

In Table 2.1, with only 13 inconsistent responses out of a total of 213 actual responses, the ratio of correctly ordered responses to total responses is

$$\text{C.R.} = 1 - \frac{13}{213} = \frac{200}{213} = 0.94$$

which is well above the 0.90 level Guttman suggested as acceptable for reproducibility.

SUBJECTIVE AND OBJECTIVE VALIDITY.   An even more difficult requirement of scientific descriptions is that they measure what they are intended to do, i.e., that they have a high degree of subjective and objective validity. Assuming that the cases in Table 2.1 were carefully selected, there are still several problems concerning the validity of its ranking of justices. At the most liberal end of the scale Justice Douglas is given a higher rank, although he has fewer votes "For" economic liberalism than Justice Black. It turns out that a rearrangement of these two justices would not improve the individual scalability. Douglas' "inconsistencies" are found in non-extreme cases, numbers 8 and 10. Putting Black first would not change these abnormalities but instead it would make Case 25 an additional inconsistency for both Black and Douglas. Following the scalability criteria, we must accept the given ordering of justices as the more plausible alternative.

Similarly, at the lower end, Clark's high number of inconsistencies do not make his ranking highly reliable, nor does the high number of Frankfurter's absences. Again, however, the ordering given seems to reduce classification errors as much as possible. (The reader is urged to try alternative issue and justice orderings, calculating reproducibilities as he goes along.)

Subjectively, the overall impression of the validity of the scale in Table 2.1 may be quite favorable (although an additional analysis of the details of the cases involved would also be desirable). The unidimensionality of judicial attitudes toward economic liberalism *is* remarkably strong, but not perfectly reproducible.

Another favorable aspect of the scale in Table 2.1 is its *ordinal* nature, which at least subjectively seems less inaccurate than an *interval* index based on the number or percentage of votes "for" economic liberalism. We have no reason to believe that *percentage* of votes accurately reflects the *degree* of liberalism. When the assumptions of a particular level of measurement have not been tested for, the scholar should usually reduce the level being used.[13]

Objectively, one can compare such findings with those of other scholars and with other sets of data. Schubert, for example, showed that his Guttman scales corresponded quite closely in both their substantive content and the ranking of justices with earlier results by Pritchett and Fellman. Considerable continuity has existed from one session of the Supreme Court to another, even though the specific facts of cases involving economic liberalism have changed.

IMPLICATIONS OF THE ABOVE ILLUSTRATION. Showing the ordinal nature of a large set of Supreme Court opinions is a good example of applying mathematics to politics. These votes directly influence the distribution of rewards and penalties in American society and as such they are important political decisions. To the extent that the operational measurements in Table 2.1 are both reliable and valid, such precise descriptions will greatly aid further attempts to explain both why these opinions are held and what their consequences might be.

Another implication of the above example is that higher levels of political measurement, although difficult to achieve, are both desirable and feasible in certain situations. Starting with crude, qualitative

[13] The problem of whether or not to reduce uncertain interval measurements to more certain ordinal ones is a complicated one. Depending on the relative amount of distortion introduced and information lost, one may sometimes be justified in maintaining interval scales and using more powerful mathematical techniques. Another approach is to transform ordinal data or uncertain interval data into an interval scale less likely seriously to distort one's results. The more advanced reader is referred to Robert Abelson and John Tukey, "Efficient Conversion of Non-Metric Information Into Metric Information," *Proceedings of the Social Statistics Section* (Washington: American Statistical Association, 1960), John B. Carroll "The Nature of the Data, or How to Choose a Correlation Coefficient," *Psychometrika*, XXVI (December 1961), pp. 347–72, and Helen Peak, "Problems of Objective Observation" in Festinger and Katz, eds., *Research Methods in the Behavioral Sciences, op. cit.*, pp. 243–99.

data, the Guttman scaling procedure finds, but does not coerce, the data into unidimensional ordinal relationships. Derived from recurring patterns of behavior, this ranking of issues and justices summarizes a good deal of useful information. In an approximate way, the Coefficient of Reproducibility indicates the closeness of fit of this one dimensional description of certain judicial attitudes.

It should also be noted that the scale itself highlights a few exceptional or deviant opinions, which may profitably be subjected to further analysis. It does not *predict* how future decisions will be made, but it does indicate that recognizable general attitudes toward economic liberalism have underlain a good number of judicial decisions. Which future issues will be interpreted along similar lines, at what point in the scale, remains at the discretion of the justices, and can probably best be explained using the reasons they themselves give.

CHAPTER 3

Measuring Inequality

> *Diluting the weight of votes because of place of residence*
> *impairs basic constitutional rights under the 14th Amendment,*
> *just as much as invidious discrimination based upon factors*
> *such as race . . . or economic status. . . .*
>
> CHIEF JUSTICE WARREN

POLITICAL PHILOSOPHERS have always tried to describe the goals of political communities. Modern political analysis has translated this quest into the problems of clarifying goals and evaluating policy alternatives. These goals are in turn described as differing value distributions, such as the various ways in which wealth, political power, and educational opportunities might be shared in our society.

Those primarily concerned with describing and explaining political behavior are faced with problems similar to those of political philosophers. Empirical researchers need to conceptualize and describe actual value outcomes in different political associations.

Both normative philosophers and empirical theorists must solve similar measurement problems—one group of scholars must carefully evaluate the alternatives they envision while the other needs accurately to assess the situations at hand. Practicing politicians, who are not always able to divide themselves so nicely into philosophic and hard-headed parts, are faced with both problems at once—they have frequently to compare the world as it is with the world as they would like it to be.

Because mathematical concepts may be defined independently of any particular content, they may be applied to a wide range of actual or potential value distributions. After defining and relating several mathematical ways of measuring the degree to which values are shared, in this chapter we shall apply them to politically relevant experience: legislative malapportionment, American income distributions before and after taxes, and racial imbalance in the public schools of New Haven, Connecticut. These situations all reveal inequalities—unequally shared values such as votes, wealth, and white classmates. In each case, actual situations will be evaluated in terms of various policy goals and alternatives.

A.   Mathematical Definitions of Inequality

EXAMPLES FROM THE LITERATURE OF POLITICS.   Ways in which value inequalities can be measured have frequently been mentioned in the literature of politics. A brief review of a few of these suggestions will help to bring some of their central aspects into focus.

Chapter 1 recalled how justice was defined by Pythagoras, Plato, and Aristotle in mathematical terms. Injustice was considered to be the lack of justice, or the violation of the various mathematical equalities with which justice was associated. Aristotle mentioned several norms against which actual injustice might be compared. One of them was the idea of democratic equality:

The democratic conception of justice is the enjoyment of arithmetical equality, and not the enjoyment of proportionate equality on the basis of desert [i.e., merit, as Aristotle himself would have preferred]. On this arithmetical conception of justice the masses must necessarily be sovereign . . .

In ideal agricultural democracies:

Equality *might* be taken to mean that the poorer class should exercise no greater authority than the rich, or in other words, that sovereignty . . . [should be] equally vested in all the citizens on a numerical basis. [Then] the upholders of democracy could afford to believe that equality—and liberty—was really achieved by their constitution.

Assuming that there are two classes which compose the state—the wealthy class and the poor, and that both classes should obey the will of the "major part" of the entire state, Aristotle suggests how justice would be secured:

[In the case when the majorities of each class disagree] we may attribute sovereignty to the will of a majority of persons *who are also the owners of a majority of property.* . . . Suppose that 6 of the 10 [members of the wealthy class] have arrived at a decision conflicting with that of 15 of the 20 [poor]. This means that the minority of 4 in the wealthy class agrees with the majority in the poorer class. . . . In that case sovereignty should rest with the will of that side [be it the side of the 6 + 5 or of the 15 + 4] whose members, on both of its elements being added together, have property in excess of that belonging to the members of the other.[1]

Jean Jacques Rousseau distinguished between "natural inequality"

---

[1] Ernest Barker, *The Politics of Aristotle* (New York: Oxford University Press, 1958), pp. 258–261. Italics in the original translation.

and "moral or political inequality" arising out of the conventions of human society. The latter he defined as consisting of

the different privileges, which some men enjoy to the prejudice of others; such as that of being more rich, more honoured, more powerful or even in a position to exact obedience.[2]

Finally, recall Lasswell's definition of an elite.

The influential are those who get the most of what there is to get. Available values may be classified as *deference, income, safety*. Those who get the most are *elite;* the rest are *mass*.[3]

Several conclusions emerge from a reading of these and other authors.

1. *Inequalities relevant to politics include those in several different value categories.* Rousseau's list mentions power, wealth, and honor (social respect), which will be studied below. Lasswell's multivalued scheme of analysis would also include skill, intellectual enlightenment, affection (family and friendship), physical and mental well-being, and moral rectitude.

2. *Political worth, or value, can at least in theory be measured with the accuracy of a ratio or an interval scale.* In his theory of proportionate equality, Aristotle implies that merit or "desert" can be measured on a ratio scale. Otherwise political representation or other rewards could not be rationed out in proportion to individual worth. The example of democratic sovereignty defined in terms of "a majority of property" also requires quantitative measurement. Recall from Chapter 2 that if citizens' properties could only be ranked in their value, adding and subtracting these values would not be allowed by the logical rules of ordinal measurement. Aristotle could not meaningfully add the wealth of rich or poor property owners unless their worth (i.e., property) was measured on at least an interval scale.[4]

[2] J. J. Rousseau, *A Dissertation on the Origin and Foundation of the Inequality of Mankind.*

[3] H. D. Lasswell, *Politics: Who Gets What, When, How* (Cleveland: World Publishing Company, 1958), p. 13.

[4] Operational definitions of other kinds of values of all kinds are sometimes also possible on an interval scale. Von Neuman and Morgenstern's *Theory of Games and Economic Behavior* (Princeton: Princeton University Press, 1944) gives a rigorous way of defining and measuring on an interval scale the value of events or objects to competing actors in risk-taking situations (see Chapter 7). S. S. Stevens in "Measurement, Psychophysics and Utility," in C. West Churchman and Philburn Ratoosh, *Measurement: Definitions and Theories* (New York: Wiley, 1959), suggests how values might be measured on ratio scales using an experimental approach.

3. *Equality and inequality can be ascribed to either individuals or collectivities.* Rousseau, for example, focuses on those individuals with more "privileges" than others. For Aristotle injustice can mean inequality between two classes in society.

4. *Individual values may be absolutely or contextually defined.* Political worth may accrue equally to every individual citizen, or it might be defined proportionately with respect to some average share of privilege or merit.

5. In studying inequality, *it is useful to cumulate both values and individuals.* Both Aristotle and Lasswell suggest adding values so that the compared populations or values constitute a majority of citizens or a major part of the values concerned.

A MATHEMATICAL FORMALIZATION. Mathematically all of the above injunctions are easy to follow. Because pure mathematics is content-free, a set of mathematical formulas for describing equality and measuring departures from it may easily be applied to different kinds of values. Both actual and desired value positions of symbolically identified individuals and groups will be defined on interval or ratio scales. If these values have these measurement properties, subtracting from them or dividing them by average or proportionate value shares should not raise any difficulty. Finally, as will be illustrated below, cumulating values held by certain proportions of the population is a key idea in the assessment of the overall inequality of a particular value distribution. Geometrically and algebraically, cumulative value distributions suggest a great variety of politically relevant measures of inequality.

Let us imagine a universe U consisting of values and individuals. Let us label each individual out of a total population of N members by an integer i (where i may equal 1, 2, ... or N). The values held by each individual will be denoted v_i and *assumed* to have the properties of either interval or ratio scales. We shall also assume that the total values in the universe (symbolized by V) equals the sum of the values held by its individual members. Using the capital form of the Greek letter *sigma* ($\sum$) as a summation sign, this assumption can be stated as a symbolic equation:

$$\sum_{i=1}^{N} v_i = v_1 + v_2 + \cdots + v_N = V \tag{3.1}$$

This equation may be read: "the sum of all v_i (from $i = 1$ all the way up to $i = N$) is equal to V."

We shall complicate our imaginary universe by also assuming that it can be completely divided up into NG distinct groups of individuals. Individuals in each group will be assumed to have equal value shares. These additional assumptions can be symbolically stated; letting j be an integer identifying any particular group ($j = 1, 2, \ldots$ or NG), we shall denote the equal values held by each member of group j as v_j. The number or frequency of members in group j will be symbolized by f_j. Equation (3.2) below indicates that total group membership adds up to the total population N. The next equation shows that multiplying each group's size by the typical value belonging to any of its members, and then summing these results for all groups, gives the value total of the universe, i.e., V.

$$\sum_{j=1}^{NG} f_j = N \tag{3.2}$$

$$\sum_{j=1}^{NG} f_j v_j = V \tag{3.3}$$

Each of these summations is for all groups ($j = 1, 2, \ldots$, and NG).

A final definition in translating the analysis of value distributions into mathematical symbols will be some way of identifying the norms or standards that are theoretically expected of an individual or group. Both moral philosophers and factual observers must compare actual distributions with those they normatively or empirically expect. For any individual i (or group j), let these expectations be symbolized by a subscripted (e_i or e_j). Mathematically, *equality means that for each individual or group the value held corresponds to the value he is expected to have:*

$$v_i = e_i \qquad (i = 1, 2, \ldots \text{ and } N) \tag{3.4}$$

For simplicity this and subsequent concepts and their symbolic definitions will be given only for individuals, although similar statements about v_j and e_j will usually apply.

Democratic equality and proportionate equality each suggest different formulas for calculating an individual's expected value position (his e_i). Letting a v with a bar over it symbolize the *average value held* $[\bar{v} = (1/N) \sum_{i=1}^{N} v_i]$, the norm of democratic equality requires each individual to have the same average amount of values:

$$e_i = \bar{v} \qquad (i = 1, 2, \ldots \text{ and } N) \tag{3.5}$$

Proportionate equality, on the other hand, requires that values be distributed in a presumably unequal fashion according to other individual characteristics, such as merit, property, knowledge, etc. (No end of debate is in sight, to be sure, on which other characteristics are appropriate, but this is not the immediate mathematical problem.) If individual merit is symbolically denoted m_i, Aristotle would expect values (like political power) to be distributed according to a constant proportion of merit:

$$e_i = k \times m_i \qquad (i = 1, 2, \ldots \text{ and } N) \qquad (3.6)$$

In Equation (3.6) k is a constant of proportion relating units of normatively expected value to units of merit.

As we shall see below, *the basic element in all mathematical definitions of inequality is some measure of the extent to which v_i does not equal e_i.* In measuring inequality we should look for the extent to which Equation (3.4) is not in fact true, using either Equation (3.5) or Equation (3.6) or some other formula to define the norm of equality.

A point of considerable importance is that, even when someone does not morally accept the goal of democratic equality, he might be willing to describe degrees of inequality in terms of deviations from the egalitarian ideal. A similar remark holds for the operationally more difficult concept of proportionate equality, a norm that will not be fully explored in the discussions below. Thus either kind of norm may serve as a theoretically useful standard for either moral or factual comparisons.

MEASURES OF INDIVIDUAL INEQUALITY.   What does it mean to say that someone is more powerful? Or enjoying more than proportionate equality in public rewards? These questions can be answered in several ways.

1. *Value Differences and Ratios.*   We already know from Chapter 2 that for interval measures of power, comparisons can be made according to interval differences. Values measured on ratio scales can even be divided or multiplied by other values in a meaningful way. Consider two individuals, Tom and Dick. Inequalities between them could be expressed as differences or ratios, that is, by

$$v_{\text{Tom}} - v_{\text{Dick}} \qquad \text{or} \qquad v_{\text{Tom}}/v_{\text{Dick}}$$

Tom, for example, might be 10 units more powerful, or two times more powerful than Dick.

If Tom and Dick were, respectively, the *most powerful* and *least powerful* individuals, their value difference (called a *range*) or their value ratio (called the *ratio of largest to smallest* values) would indicate the extremes of the entire population.[5]

2. *Differences from the Average.* Using the definition of democratic equality in Equation (3.5), individual inequality can be defined by subtracting from actual values held the expected, i.e. the average, level of values held in the population. Those with above average value positions could be considered "privileged," while those below average are clearly "discriminated against." Because for universes different from U the average value ($\bar{v}$) may be of a different level, $v_i - \bar{v}$ may take on different values in different universes. In other words, the meaning of privilege and discrimination depends on the context for which they are defined.

3. *Ratios of Advantage.* Values defined according to ratio scales can meaningfully be divided by value standards. Ratios of advantage ($v_i/\bar{v}$) can also be thought of as contextually defined indices of individual privilege or discrimination.

An interesting comparison between interval and ratio scales of measurement arises at this point. Interval scales with arbitrary zero points cannot meaningfully be divided or multiplied by other interval scales. What about intervally measured differences from an average? The answer is yes, *if* the mean (i.e., average) value in a particular distribution is considered a non-arbitrary zero point. Measuring inequality against an egalitarian ideal means does just this. Value positions are redefined as above or below average, i.e., as privileged or discriminatory. The expression $v_i - \bar{v}$ now has a meaningful zero point (perfect equality) even if the original value scale of the v_i did not.

*If we want to compare these differences in two different universes, we could standardize them, dividing them by their respective $\bar{v}$'s. Symbolically, such an expression would be

$$\frac{v_i - \bar{v}}{\bar{v}} = \frac{v_i}{\bar{v}} - 1 \qquad (3.7)$$

It turns out from the algebraic manipulation indicated in Equation (3.7) that expressing *differences* as fractions of an overall standard gives results very similar to *ratios* of advantage. In fact, subtracting 1 from

[5] As applied to different electoral districts, the *ratio of largest to smallest* voting representations has frequently been used to measure legislative malapportionment. See, for example, Andrew Hacker, *Congressional Districting: The Issue of Equal Representation* (Washington, D.C.: The Brookings Institution, 1963), p. 23, and the sources he cites.

a ratio of advantage gives a standardized difference from a mean. We need not know whether v_i is really twice as big as $\bar{v}$ in order to say that the differences from a mean are an exact proportion of the mean. This result will be very helpful in comparing different ways of measuring inequality in entire value distributions.

CUMULATIVE MEASURES OF INEQUALITY. Cumulative measures enable the observer to measure the fraction of total values held by various proportions of the population. When presented geometrically, they suggest a great variety of individual and collective measures of inequality.

1. *The Lorenz Curve.* Cumulative value distributions start by ranking all individuals according to their ratios of advantage. Ratios for groups of individuals can be calculated by an equivalent procedure, dividing the percentage of values they hold by the percentage of population they represent. Starting with those most discriminated against, a line is drawn representing the total percentage of values held by increasingly larger percentages of the population. A hypothetical curve of this sort, called a Lorenz curve, is shown in Figure 3.1.

In the picture as drawn, the $\sum v_i$ for the poorest half of the population is only 20 percent of V, while on the other hand, the wealthiest 10 percent of the population has 50 percent of obtainable values. Going along the Lorenz curve in this fashion indicates in a comprehensive way the extent to which various groups have more or less than their proportionate share of values.

The 45-degree line in Figure 3.1 represents a norm of complete, democratic equality. It indicates how values *should* be distributed if all v_i were actually equal to $\bar{v}$. As shown in the figure, complete equality means that both the poorest and wealthiest halves of the population have equal shares of the universe's total values. Other moral or factual expectations could be represented in a similar manner. Some other Lorenz curve, perhaps even the one drawn in Figure 3.1, could be used as a standard for evaluating the overall pattern of inequality. In fact, if the curved line in Figure 3.1 resulted from a distribution of values according to Aristotle's calculations of merit and Equation (3.6), then he could say that an *actual* cumulative distribution looking like the line of equality was far too egalitarian!

2. *The Slopes Curve.* Both ratios of advantage and differences from the average can be measured on a Lorenz curve. To show why this is true, it will only be necessary to talk about ratios of advantage [because of the equivalence between these two kinds of measures established in Equation (3.7) above]. *The basic result is that ratios of advantage are*

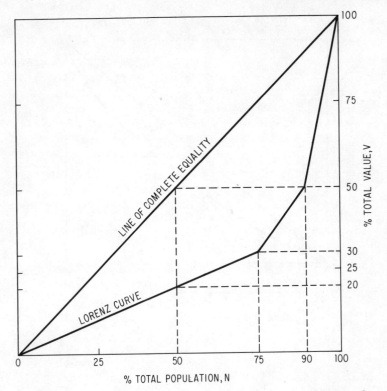

FIGURE 3.1 A Lorenz Curve of values held·by cumulative proportions of a population.

slopes of a Lorenz curve. It is easy to explain why this is so. A slope of a line is obtained by dividing a vertical rise by the corresponding horizontal distance. For a particular individual this ratio is the percentage of the total values he holds divided by the percentage of the total population he represents, i.e.,

$$\frac{100\left(v_i \bigg/ \sum_{i=1}^{N} v_i\right)}{100(1/N)}$$

Reducing this expression to simplest terms gives the ratio of advantage $v_i/\bar{v}$. Slopes of the Lorenz curve may be approximated visually or plotted separately, as shown in Figure 3.2.

3. *The Equal Share Coefficient.* An important change in the Lorenz curve occurs when its slope, the ratio of advantage, equals and begins

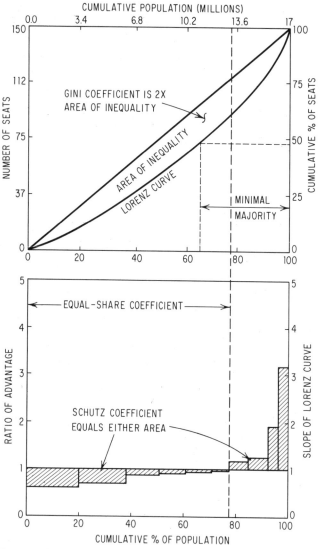

FIGURE 3.2 A Lorenz Curve and related "Slopes Curve" for the apportionment of the New York State Assembly 1960. (*Source: See note 10.*)

to exceed one. People to the right of this point on the curve get more than an equal share in the allocation of values. People to the left get less than their (equal) share. It is thus possible to define an *equal share coefficient* as equal to the percentage of the population getting something less than an equal share of values. In Figure 3.1, this would be 75 percent of the population. Bruce Russett and the present author have suggested interpreting the remaining population percentage (in this case 25 percent) as the size of the middle and upper classes. *In egalitarian terms, the equal share coefficient measures the percentage size of the underprivileged population.*[6] Certainly, where a society is polarized into two classes such an interpretation would be appropriate. In other, more complicated universes, *double-share* or *triple-share coefficients* might also be useful.

4. *The Minimal Majority.* Lasswell's definition of an elite identifies those who get the *most*, not those who get more than an equal share. If our value units were legislative votes, it would be equivalent to refer to a *minimal majority*, the smallest number of individuals controlling a majority of the legislature. For the Lorenz curve in Figure 3.1, the minimal majority is 10 percent of the population. In a similar fashion one could measure the size of the population holding the top 10 percent of values, and so on.

5. *Summing Differences and Ratios.* Measures using more information regarding a cumulative value distribution are likely to be more reliable in characterizing entire distributions. Summing value differences or ratios of advantage gives more comprehensive measures of inequality than indices like the range or the largest/smallest ratio defined above.

What differences and ratios might we sum? Three possibilities suggested by the Lorenz curve come to mind, each of which leads to a famous measure of inequality. First, for interval level measurements, why not sum differences from value standards—as defined in Equation (3.4)? In the case where the e_i's equal $\bar{v}$, however, summing for all i is of no avail:

$$\sum_{i=1}^{N} (v_i - \bar{v}) = \sum_{i=1}^{N} v_i - \sum_{i=1}^{N} \bar{v} = N \cdot \frac{\sum v_i}{N} - N \cdot \bar{v} = 0 \qquad (3.8)$$

Equation (3.8) shows that the mean value $\bar{v}$ has the property that summing deviations on both sides of the mean will always give 0! On the average, the negative deviations cancel out the positive ones. A more

[6] This coefficient (actually its percentage complement) was first suggested in H. R. Alker, Jr., and B. M. Russett, "On Measuring Inequality," *Behavioral Science*, **9**, 3 (July 1964), pp. 207–18. Most of the remaining coefficients of inequality discussed in this chapter, and original sources, are given in this article.

meaningful approach would be to sum deviations, *ignoring their signs*. The mean deviation measure of inequality has been defined in just this way, dividing by the number of cases:

$$\text{Mean deviation} = \frac{1}{N} \cdot \sum_{i=1}^{N} |v_i - \bar{v}| \tag{3.9}$$

The vertical bars in this expression refer to the absolute (positive) value of the difference $v_i - \bar{v}$, regardless of whether it is positive or negative.

If the v_i varied widely, so would their mean deviation. To facilitate comparison of value distributions, expressions like the above are often normalized or standardized so as to range between 0 and 1. A *normalized mean deviation* can be defined in this manner as

$$\text{Normalized mean deviation} = \frac{1}{N} \cdot \frac{\displaystyle\sum_{i=1}^{N} |v_i - \bar{v}|}{\displaystyle\sum_{i=1}^{N} v_i} \tag{3.10}$$

Because of the identity between a normalized $(v_i - \bar{v})/\bar{v}$ and $(v_i/\bar{v}) - 1$, it is not surprising that summing ratios of advantage, i.e. adding the slopes of different segments of a Lorenz curve, will give a coefficient essentially the same as the normalized mean *deviation*. To avoid the problem of summing to zero, it is necessary to sum the ratio $v_i/\bar{v}$ only where it is greater than or less than one, but not both. *R. R. Schutz's coefficient of inequality*, a second type of summing measure, sums ratios of advantage above *or* below the equal share point (at which $v_i = \bar{v}$):

$$\text{Schutz coefficient} = \sum_{v_i \geq \bar{v}} \left(\frac{v_i}{\bar{v}} - 1 \right) = \sum_{v_i \leq \bar{v}} \left(1 - \frac{v_i}{\bar{v}} \right) \tag{3.11}$$

In Equation (3.11) the summations are above or below the equal share point of the population. Of course when $v_i = \bar{v}$, then both parentheses in Equation (3.11) equal zero. The equivalence between the two expressions in Equation (3.11) can be easily derived from Equation (3.8) (try it!).[7]

As an indication of the degree of inequality evidenced by the cumulative distribution, it is geometrically appealing to calculate the area between the Lorenz curve and the line of equality. Dividing this "*area*

---

[7] I have also shown in Alker and Russett, *op. cit.*, that, when values and populations are expressed in percentage terms, the Schutz coefficient equals fifty times the normalized mean deviation.

of inequality" by its maximum size gives a third measure, *Gini's co-efficient of inequality.* Said another way, the Gini index sums, for each individual in the population, the difference between where he is on the Lorenz curve and where he would be expected to be in the case of democratic equality. This sum is divided by its maximum possible value so that the Gini coefficient ranges between 0 and 1.

Mathematically, the formula for the Gini index can most easily be expressed in terms of two fractional variables X_i and Y_i, corresponding respectively, to coordinates of the horizontal and vertical axes of a Lorenz diagram (as in Figure 3.1):

$$X_i = \frac{i}{N} \quad \text{and} \quad Y_i = \sum_{k \leq i} v_k / V \qquad (3.12)$$

To compute the area between the actual cumulative distribution and the standard 45-degree line of equality, one can sum the areas of rectangles representing cumulatively the inequality of each individual or group. Let the height of the line of equality corresponding to the location of an individual i, be E_i. It will in fact equal the sum of all democratically expected values of individuals to the left of i, expressed as a fraction of the value total V. Using k as a convenient index of summation for these people [as in Equation (3.12)], thus

$$E_i = \sum_{k \leq i} e_k / V \qquad (3.13)$$

Finally, for each individual, we need to know the width of his vertical segment of the area of inequality. This answer—let us call it ΔX_i—read "delta-X sub i"—is just that fraction of the X axis where he belongs:

$$\Delta X_i = X_i - X_{i-1} \qquad (i = 1, \ldots, N) \qquad (3.14)$$

When $i - 1 = 0$, X is of course 0.

With these conventions, adopted so that both axes range from 0 to 1, it is possible to give three equivalent definitions of the Gini index. The maximum value of the area above the cumulative Lorenz curve is that of the triangle beneath the line of equality: one-half its base times its height, or simply $\frac{1}{2}$. Normalizing (dividing) the actual area of inequality by $\frac{1}{2}$ we have

$$\text{Gini index} = 2 \cdot \text{area of inequality} \qquad (3.15a)$$

Expressing this area approximately as the sum of rectangles with heights $E_i - Y_i$ and widths ΔX_i,

$$\text{Gini index} = 2 \sum_{i=1}^{N} (E_i - Y_i) \Delta X_i \qquad (3.15b)$$

Since we are assuming here that the E_i forms a straight line, the line of complete equality with a slope of 1, the E_i will, for our purposes, equal $1 \cdot X_i$. Therefore, we have

$$\text{Gini index} = 2 \sum_{i=1}^{N} (X_i - Y_i) \Delta X_i \qquad (3.15c)$$

B.   Unequal Votes, Taxes, and Schools

The *abstractness* of the mathematical ideas like those in the above hypothetical exercise accounts for the wide range of their applicability. As ways of describing and evaluating various policy alternatives several of the measures defined above will now be applied to a variety of political situations. We have already seen how the Lorenz curve presentation of cumulative distributions allows explicit, visual comparisons between *actual* and empirically or normatively *expected* value distributions. This feature of Lorenz curves (and of the corresponding slopes curves) strongly recommend their use in political analysis. In the example below, a Lorenz curve for legislative malapportionment, a slopes curve for alternative public tax laws, and a Lorenz curve comparing actual racial imbalance with a proposed solution illustrate the value of this approach.[8]

LEGISLATIVE MALAPPORTIONMENT IN NEW YORK.   In their epic 1964 decision on legislative apportionment (*Reynolds* v. *Sims*, etc.) the Supreme Court majority declared that "the fundamental principle of representative government in this country is one of equal representation for equal numbers of people, without regard to race, sex, economic status, or place of residence within a state."[9]   Both houses of state legislatures were required to meet this test, and as a result apportionments in Alabama, New York, Maryland, Virginia, Delaware, and Colorado were held unconstitutional.   Many of the arguments by the

---

[8] Other measures, like the largest/smallest values ratio, lose a good deal of relevant information about the overall shape of a distribution.   Even the minimal majority measure talks about a single point on a curve, but it at least appears to reflect the overall shape of a Lorenz curve more accurately than do measures based on the highest and/or lowest units alone. (See Alker and Russett, *op. cit.*, for details.)   Glendon Schubert and Charles Press, "Measuring Malapportionment," *American Political Science Review*, LVIII, 2 (June 1964), pp. 302–27, have impressively analyzed all American state legislatures using varieties of the mean deviation (involving squared, cubed and fourth-power deviations). Although their approach is commendably comprehensive, it does not lend itself so easily to graphic or verbal statements of policy alternatives defined in a cumulative fashion.

[9] All quotations from this decision have been taken from *The New York Times*, June 16, 1964, pp. 28–31.

majority of the Court used some of the measures of inequality that have already been discussed. We shall illustrate them and several alternatives by reference to a Lorenz curve and the corresponding slopes curve for the New York State Assembly in 1960. (See Figure 3.2).[10] This geometric way of describing and evaluating malapportionment is especially appropriate because the Court has accepted the norm of democratic equality, which in the Lorenz curve of Figure 3.2 is again indicated by a 45-degree line of equality.

One additional comment about the validity of this approach may be helpful. Justice Stewart, in dissent, asserted that "nobody's right to vote has been denied . . . nobody has been deprived of the right to have his vote counted." The majority, on the other hand, joined Justice Warren in saying that "diluting the weight of votes because of place of residence impairs basic rights under the 14th Amendment. . . ." What is the difference between these two views? One of them clearly thinks of the "right to vote" as "present" or "absent," a qualitative attribute; the other sees it as something *more* or *less* enjoyed in a quantitative fashion. If the representation of an individual from one county cannot be compared with that of another, then the following analysis would not apply. We must therefore assume that operational definitions like the fraction of seats per population fraction, or the fraction of a representative held by a voting individual, are valid measures on a ratio scale of the right to vote.

The Court asks rhetorically, "can one person be given twice or ten times the voting power of another. . .?" In Figure 3.2 we see that the top 3 percent of the population has ratios of advantage greater than 3.0. Their votes count three times as much as those of the average citizen! As shown by the slopes curve in the lower half of the figure, the next highest 5 percent of the population is about twice as powerful as the average. Looking again at the Lorenz curve, we see that this top 8 percent of the population (in absolute terms, about 1.2 million voters) has 20 percent of the representative strength in the Assembly.

The Court is unable to "sanction minority control of state legislative bodies." Compared with other states, New York's Assembly is not atypically unequal.[11] Yet the (grouped) data in Figure 3.2 indicate

---

[10] Data have been taken from Ruth Silva, "Apportionment of the New York State Legislature," *American Political Science Review*, LV, 4 (December 1961), pp. 870–881, Table XIV. They have been grouped into ten approximately equal categories of 15 seats each.

[11] *Compendium on Apportionment* (Washington, D.C.: National Municipal League, 1962), actually indicates that 30 out of 48 state lower houses had smaller minimal majorities than did the New York Assembly.

that 35 percent of the state's population, all from the *most* overrepresented counties, have potential majority control of the Assembly. The equal share coefficient further tells us that 77 percent of the population is underrepresented in the legislature, although until we get down to the "poorest" 38 percent, they all have approximately 90 percent of their "right to vote" or better.[12]

What about cumulative measures of malapportionment? The minimal majority measure (which is partly cumulative) was used by the Court, and so in fact were average ratios of advantage for population subgroups. Regarding the New York Senate, the Warren opinion refers to the average population of the senatorial districts in the "populous counties" and in the "less populous counties." It goes on to say that "a citizen in a less populous county had under the 1953 apportionment, over 1.5 times the representation, on the average, of a citizen in a populous county. . . ." *The Court is thus averaging ratios of advantages, very much in the manner of a standardized mean deviation or a Schutz coefficient.* If "the less populous" counties are those below the equal share point, the correspondence would be exact, if only a denominator term were used to normalize the result. Such normalization would in fact facilitate comparisons with other states in attempting to see which suffered from a greater degree of malapportionment. (The Schutz coefficient for the example is very easily obtained if we sum ratios of advantage above unity at the right end of the slopes curve: approximately it equals

$$3(3.4 - 1) + 5(2.0 - 1) + 8(1.25 - 1) + 7(1.20 - 1) = 15.6$$

The Court also refers to points on the Lorenz curve, or a rough approximation to it. They are hampered by the particulars of the case because they can only refer to the share of seats held by the counties where the appellants reside: "According to 1960 census figures, the six counties [where they reside] had a citizen population of 9,129,180, or 56.2 per cent of the . . . total. . . . They [the appellants] are currently represented by 72 Assemblymen . . . 48 percent of the Assembly. . . ." Looking at the Lorenz curve in Figure 3.2, we find that the *most* underrepresentative 56 percent of the citizen population has about 41 percent of the Assembly seats, a more unequal situation than cumulating for

[12] Applying a rule suggested by a committee of the American Political Science Association, that all legislative districts should not depart from the average level of representation by more than 10 percent, the slopes curve in Figure 3.2 indicates that all 23 percent of the population above the equal share point would have to be redistricted, as would the most underrepresented 38 percent. Other policy alternatives could of course be indicated by horizontal lines of various heights cutting across the slopes curve.

the plaintives alone (our data, however, may not be strictly comparable with the Court's).

A comprehensive way of stating the *overall* inequality indicated by the Lorenz curve would be to find what proportion the actual area of inequality is of the entire possible area of inequality. The approximate value for the Gini coefficient of 0.22, indicates that New York's Assembly is 22/100 of the way toward complete inequality in this particular geometric sense. Other Assemblies, we suspect, would be worse.[13] Again, the Court could facilitate such comparisons by using measures (like the minimal majority, the Schutz coefficient, or the Gini coefficient) that are independent of the particular population and legislative sizes being measured.

INCOME EQUALITY, BEFORE AND AFTER TAXES. There is a good deal of emotional argument surrounding the extremes of wealth and poverty in any country. How burdensome the inequality of wealth is depends, of course, on the social and human costs of low incomes and the other opportunities forgone as a result of an unequal distribution of wealth. Those favoring the inequality of wealth cite its supposed stimulant effect on the poor and other favorable economic consequences, such as the excellence made possible in private and public life.

Even more emotions are energized on the subject of taxation. Poor and middle income groups complain of their burdens, asking for greater "progressive" tax burdens placed on the wealthy. The defenders of the poor call for at least a partial redistribution of wealth. As a result a tax structure exists which, after all deductions, exemptions, and capital gains and losses have been taken into account, theoretically, taxes million dollar incomes between 80 and 90 percent.

The measures we have already used to study malapportionment can also be used to study the distribution of income in American society, and the effects of our supposedly progressive tax structure.

First, it is possible to compare American income distributions with those of other countries using comprehensive indices like the Gini coefficient. Unfortunately, comparable data are not always available for this purpose. Nonetheless, in a recent careful examination of income distributions before taxes in 20 mostly developed countries, it was found that the American Gini index for 1956 was about 0.40, ranking 13th.[14] Compared with other nations, the United States does not appear atypically unequal. [Note, in passing, the interesting possibility

---

[13] Alker and Russett, *op. cit.*, found 18 out of 27 *state senates* to have higher Gini coefficients of inequality.

[14] Russett and Alker, Deutsch, Lasswell, *World Handbook of Political and Social Indicators* (New Haven: Yale University Press, 1964), p. 174.

that, if New York is typical, formal political power (representation) in a democracy may be more equally shared than income and wealth. Cumulative indices of value concentration allow provocative comparisons of value distributions in different contexts.]

What effect do taxes have on the inequality of incomes? In other words, how progressive is the tax structure—to what extent does it place heavier burdens on the rich and reduce overall income inequality? Answers to this kind of question depend heavily on the data available. Fortunately, the National Committee on Governmental Finance has recently provided more accurate answers to these kind of questions than heretofore were possible.[15] *The result of a comparison of the degree of inequality in income before and after taxes is that there was remarkably little change as a result of the then effective tax structure.* To be specific, in 1960 the Gini index before taxes was 0.45, while after taxes it was 0.43!

Plotting Lorenz curves for incomes before and after taxes (as reported to the government) reveals almost no change in the slope of the curve except for a small increase in equality at the upper end of the income distribution. To get a better idea of the overall pattern involved, the slopes curve for income before taxes has been plotted in Figure 3.3, with an enlarged insert for the top 5 percent of the tax returns. The average income per tax return is about $6,000. With this information we see, for example, that about 35 percent of the tax returns show incomes of less than half the average and that about 65 percent of the returns show less than this amount (this latter percentage is the size of the equal share coefficient). At the other end about 10 percent of the returns are more than twice the average, while less than 1 percent of the tax returns report incomes over $60,000.

What about the effects of tax structure? Looking carefully at the insert we see that it is only the top 1 percent of the income receivers

[15] The data reported here were made available to the author by Mr. George Sadowsky of Yale, Dr. Joseph Pechman of The Brookings Institution, and the National Committee on Government Finance, which supervises Brookings' Studies of Government Finance. They result from a computer analysis of approximately 100,000 tax returns made up of a sample of adjusted gross incomes below $100,000 combined with a complete enumeration for those incomes in the higher tax brackets. Exact correspondence with the earlier Gini coefficient for income before taxes should not be expected because (1) income may not have the same meaning in both examples; (2) the earlier data may have been grouped differently and less accurately; (3) the earlier data are for 1956, not 1960; and (4) the present results are for a population of tax returns (whether individually or jointly filed), not individuals. A curve similar to Figure 3.4, but only for taxable returns, has been published in Richard Goode, *The Individual Income Tax*, The Brookings Institution, Washington, D.C., 1964, p. 236.

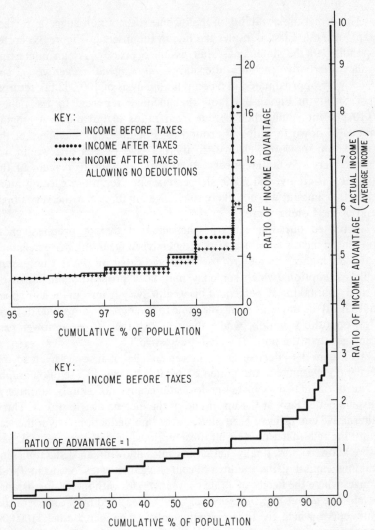

FIGURE 3.3 Ratios of income advantage before and after taxes. (*Source: See note 15.*)

which are noticeably decreased in their share of the wealth. Before taxes most of them have about 6 times more than average; afterwards the figure is close to 5. Among the top tenth of a percent of the population, on the average, the decrease is also slight, from a ratio of income advantage near 19 to one close to 16. It should be clear why the Gini coefficients before and after taxes were so remarkably similar. Only the very upper end of the Lorenz curve is noticably affected.

This remarkable stability in the income distribution suggests further explorations. First, consider the line in the insert in Figure 3.3 corresponding to the statement "after assumed taxes." As an interesting policy alternative incomes after taxes, *allowing no deductions of any kind*, were approximated in a computer analysis of 100,000 tax returns. The results in Figure 3.3 show that incomes reported by the richest 0.10 percent would then be cut from ratios of advantage averaging about 16 down to ratios of around 8. For the other members of the population, however, changes in the tax laws of this sort would not have a very substantial effect. Because only about 10 percent of the tax returns are over $12,000, steeper tax rates for those earning more than this amount are not likely to change anything but the very upper end of the Lorenz curve.

A related question concerns the actual degree of progressiveness present in the tax structure. Tax progressivism means higher percentage rates for higher income groups. It is predicated on the not unreasonable assumption (which someday may be a proposition that can be tested) that taking 50 percent of his wealth away from a millionaire does not "hurt" as much as doing the same to someone earning 4000 dollars. The opposite situation, where the rich pay their taxes at lower percentages than the poor, is called "regressive."

In Figure 3.4 effective taxes, in percentages of income given to the Federal government, are plotted on what is known as a semilog graph. (The horizontal axis increases logarithmically, not simply additively, given a better look at the upper end of the income distribution.) Three alternative curves have been plotted: the "no deductions" hypothetical rate; the rate that would result if exemptions, deductions, and sick pay were allowed; and, finally, actual tax rates allowing all deductions, including capital gains credits. Progressive tax rates occur in those ranges where the height of a rate curve increases with increasing income level. The *degree of progressiveness* can be measured by the *slope* of the rates curve, which gives the percentage of tax rate increase per $100,000 income increase. It should be clear to the reader that non-logarithmic graph paper would give the same numerical measure of progressiveness, but would not give the same overall visual impression of the steepness of the slope.

As mentioned earlier, tax returns below $10,000–$12,000 seem to have similar slopes before and after exemptions, etc. For these 90 percent of all individuals or families, capital gains do not appreciably affect their effective tax rates. To the right of the $10,000 gross income level, however, we see that both the no deductions tax structure and

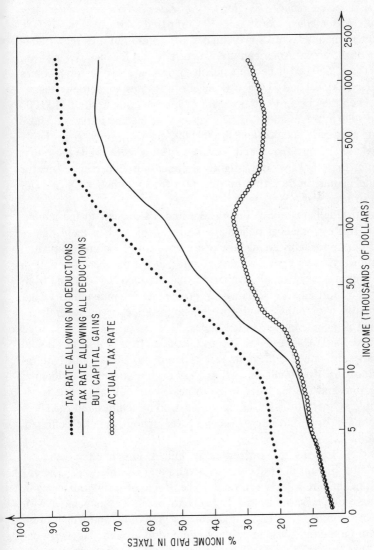

FIGURE 3.4   The effects of various deductions on the American tax structure in 1960.   (*Source: See note 15.*)

a rate structure in which only capital gains deductions are not allowed rise quite steeply to rates between 70 and 90 percent. *Capital gains credits, however, reduce the effective tax rates for people earning over $100,000 by something like 50 percent!* Compared to those below $10,000, all higher income returns pay higher tax rates, but the remarkable nature of the actual American tax structure is that for incomes between $10,000 and $50,000 it is quite steeply progressive, while for incomes between $100,000 and $1,000,000 the effective rates are actually regressive. Then they begin to go up again. Those making around $100,000 pay (on the average) about 32 percent of their income in taxes. Those making between $500,000 and $1,000,000, most of which is probably non-salaried income from capital gains, pay 24 percent, while those that do better than that owe only slightly more, about 29 percent. Senator Douglas claims, in fact, that no one pays the hypothetical maximum, which in 1960 was a 90% rate.

Ethical judgments about Figures 3.3 and 3.4 are left to the reader. The several hypothetical policy alternatives indicated in these figures would not appreciably change the overall pattern of income inequality, only the very upper end. We have found that the number of people in these ranges is very small; it appears that tax incomes resulting from changes in current capital gains tax provisions for individuals would not greatly alter either total government revenue or the overall inequality of income in the United States.

RACIAL IMBALANCE IN NEW HAVEN'S JUNIOR HIGH SCHOOLS.   Racial imbalance in public education results from more than outright intimidation; in the North, as well as the South, patterns of residential segregation and the tendency to go to nearby schools are partially responsible. Other problems, like poor classroom facilities and the effect on morale of being put into a "second-class" school, are also definitely involved.

For these reasons, it is operationally difficult to define the degree of segregation present in any school in a valid and reliable way. The approach taken here will concentrate on the degree of racial imbalance in the classroom, a variable that is likely to be closely associated with many of the other aspects of educational segregation, and which often seems to be the most visible point of contention in many Northern debates over the redistricting of public schools. Operationally, the percentage of white classmates is thus assumed to be a valued good, in exactly the same way that income and voting representation were in the previous illustrations.

Relevant data for four different junior high schools in New Haven, Connecticut, are given in Table 3.1. The numbers of whites, non-whites, and total students in each school are first presented. With these data, cumulative percentages for the entire junior high school population of New Haven can be calculated. These percentages and their ratio are given in the last three columns of the table.

It may be recalled from the previous discussion of the slopes curve that the ratio of the percentage of white students to the percentage of all students is a ratio of advantage. These ratios show that Bassett has proportionally less than one-fifth as many whites as do all the schools on the average, while Sheridan and Fair Haven have about 40 percent more than is typical.

In Figure 3.5, we can consider both the cumulative extent of racial imbalance in these schools and the effects of a proposed plan for improving racial balance. Visually, unlike the tax reform alternatives mentioned previously, it is clear that the school board's proposal goes a long way toward removing racial imbalance. Whereas in June 1964 only 9 percent of Bassett's students were white (they amounted to 3 percent of the entire population of white students), the proposal suggests changing this proportion to 50 percent. The proposed change is so significant that the Bassett school will no longer have the highest

Table 3.1. **The actual racial breakdown of students in New Haven's four junior high schools, June, 1964.** *

	Number of Students			*Cumulative Percentages*		
	Whites	*Non-whites*	*Total*	*% of all Whites*	*% of all Students*	*% Whites/ % Students*
Bassett	55	555	610	3	17	0.18
Troup	419	514	933	19	27	0.70
Sheridan	741	148	889	34	25	1.36
Fair Haven	968	140	1108	44	31	1.42
Total	2183	1357	3540	100	100	1.0 (weighted average)

* These data are taken from a frank and commendably courageous document issued by the New Haven Public Schools, Dr. Laurence G. Paquin, Superintendent, June 8, 1964, entitled *Proposals for Promoting Equality of Educational Opportunity and Dealing with the Problems of Racial Imbalance*, pp. 10–11. A plan similar in most respects to the proposal discussed below was eventually voted into effect by the school board.

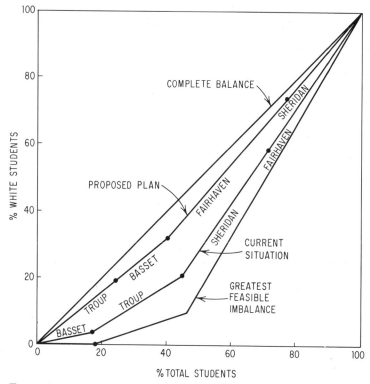

FIGURE 3.5   Four alternative patterns of racial imbalance in New Haven junior high schools. (*Source: See note 16.*)

degree of racial imbalance. Perfect racial equality would have all four schools with whites in a 3:2 majority (see the totals in Table 3.1); the proposed plan, by hitting heavily at the worst area of inequality, would move the Lorenz curve quite close to democratic equality.

The actual degree of improvement of racial balance can best be indicated by measures like the Gini or Schutz coefficients. After performing the required calculations, we find that the current situation corresponds to a Gini index of 0.25, while the proposal as sketched in Figure 3.5 would mean a much smaller Gini index of 0.09. These numbers indicate that the proposal is certainly more than a "token reform": it would cut racial imbalance by more than half.

An additional way of evaluating the proposed change is with respect to the worst possible situation. The hypothetical Lorenz curve resulting from "moving" as many Negroes as possible into Bassett and Troup is also given in Figure 3.5. It indicates the maximum feasible racial imbalance when school sizes are kept the same and the non-whites are kept in the non-white schools as much as possible. The Gini coefficient for this curve is about 0.40. Dividing 0.09 and 0.25 by this figure gives 0.23 and 0.63, respectively. In words, the policy alternative proposed to the New Haven School Board would decrease racial imbalance in New Haven junior high schools from 63 to 23 percent; it would bring the school system three-quarters of the way toward the egalitarian democratic goal of complete racial balance.

CHAPTER 4

Two-variable Relationships

It is for the collectors of data to know the fact and for the mathematicians to establish the reason.

ARISTOTLE, *The Organum*

IF EVENTS ARE UNIQUE, repetitive observation is impossible; to the extent that events are describable and comparable, a science about measurable political characteristics is feasible. The main goals of such a science are objective descriptions, explanations, and predictions. It seeks to formulate and test hypotheses, sometimes embodied in general deductive theories, about conditions affecting political processes and their outcomes.

Mathematical formalization is especially helpful in stating and testing vague or controversial hypotheses. It forces the scientist explicitly and consistently to take into account the explanatory variables that he feels are related to a particular set of events; more importantly, mathematical treatment requires an exact specification or formula that states *how* such variables affect the variable being explained. For these purposes quantitative descriptions are extremely helpful. In thinking about the influence of the rural-urban split on legislative apportionment, for example, a completely precise theoretical statement would say that ratios of legislative advantage will be related in a linear fashion to the percentage of each county's rural population, that 10 percent increases in urbanization will decrease ratios of legislative advantage by 20 percent, that 90 percent of the legislative districts will have their ratios of advantage explained within 10 percent of the actual value by such a theory, and so on. Such statements allow the skeptic and the believer to see at just what point they differ in theory and to what extent.

Even more significant, however, in such a controversy are the ways in which mathematical analysis of data can be used to test and reject controversial hypotheses. *If* Aristotle hypothesizes, on the bases of his general reflections about politics, that certain kinds of international behavior will cause wars, is he or is he not correct? And to what extent? When data purporting to test this hypothesis have been collected, ways of measuring the proposed explanatory relationships are still required.

Statistics is a branch of mathematics particularly relevant to the study of politics, "the science that teaches us the political arrangement of all the states," as its original meaning suggests. One branch of the subject, *descriptive statistics*, includes problems of describing and measuring the characteristics of different sets of data, using such techniques as Guttman scales and cumulative distributions. Descriptive statistics is also useful in precisely stating or describing relations between different variables, such as urbanism and malapportionment. Another branch, *inductive statistics*, is concerned with making and testing generalizations. As used by social scientists, this often amounts to stating the risks of accepting or rejecting certain hypotheses about a larger universe of information on the bases of results calculated for a smaller and presumably random selection of data. Some of the relations between the problems of inductive generalization and political judgment are discussed in the Appendix.

Because political scientists often do not have random samples of data, but rather complete or nearly complete information about a particular universe (city, state, or international system) during a certain time period, this chapter as well as the next two chapters are focused on ways in which explanatory theories about politics can be stated and tested by using some traditional and modern tools of descriptive statistical analysis. The present chapter concentrates on the methods of of two-variable correlation and regression analysis, and the next chapter briefly illustrates how such techniques and models may be applied to complex, many-variable situations. Chapter 6, which logically follows from these discussions, reviews methods of distinguishing causal from spurious explanations.

A. Relationships between Attributes

Let us first illustrate mathematical ways of explaining one qualitative variable in terms of another with a hypothetical example based on an incident discussed in Chapter 1. While reasoning about why Persia attacked Athens in 490 B.C., Aristotle asserted a law of universal validity. From this law, "war is made on those who commit an aggressive wrong," he syllogistically deduced that Athens would be attacked because she had committed unprovoked aggression against Persia. His discussion centered on two state characteristics: the attribute of being a wrong aggressor and the attribute of being attacked. His law between those two predicates can be restated as follows: no examples of "unprovoked aggression (*B*)" can be found of which it is not also true that "they are attacked (*A*)."[1]

Let us suppose that Aristotle knew the history of 150 city-states (this number of constitutions were reportedly collected by him and his students). Furthermore, let us agree that a certain number of them, say 50, had committed unprovoked aggression (a concept that is, of course, very difficult to measure). In effect, we are saying that the predicate or attribute "unprovoked aggressor" is *distributed* among these states with the following *marginal frequencies:*

Attribute	Frequency
Unprovoked aggressor	50
Justified aggressor or non-aggressor	100
Total number of states	150

What distribution should we assume for the predicate "being attacked?" Since there are both provoked and unprovoked attacks, we should expect that more than 50 cities had been attacked, some of them by the same aggressor. For illustrative purposes, then let us assume 75 cities were attacked and 75 were not. The corresponding *marginal frequency distribution* is:

Attribute	Frequency
Has been attacked	75
Has not been attacked	75
Total number of city-states	150

Aristotle claims these two attributes are conditionally related. To describe this relationship consider the data displayed in Table 4.1. Each table cross-tabulates the frequency of one attribute in the presence or absence of the other. When an attribute is absent a bar is placed

---

[1] In modern logical notation (see Chapter 1), if *Bad* (*X*) means "*X* is a bad aggressor" and *Attacked* (*X*) means "*X* is attacked," Aristotle can be interpreted as asserting

$$\sim (EX)[\text{Bad } (X) \cdot \sim \text{Attacked } (X)]$$

In words, "There is no state *X* that is both a bad aggressor and is not attacked." Using sentence symbols, *p* to refer to "a state is attacked" and *q* to mean "a state commits wrong aggression," this same relationship may be symbolized

$$\sim (q \cdot \sim p)$$

This claim is equivalent to the *conditional* relationship defined in logical symbols as

$$p \supset q$$

and read as "*p* horseshoe *q*" or "*p* implies *q*." It means the same thing as Aristotle's "*B* applies to *A*."

over the relevant letter. For two dichotomous (two-part) attributes, such displays are called "2 × 2 contingency tables." The "dependent" attribute (which is to be explained) is presented vertically on the left of the tables, while the "independent" (explanatory) attribute is labeled horizontally.

The first hypothetical case in Table 4.1 shows the *marginal distributions* of the two attributes that have just been described. The unspecified

Table 4.1. **Relationships between unprovoked aggression (A) and being attacked (B) in a hypothetical universe of 150 Greek city-states.**

Case 1 *Marginal distributions with unspecified cell entries*

		A Aggressor	$\bar{A}$ Non-aggressor		
B	Attacked	a	b	$a + b =$	75
$\bar{B}$	Not attacked	c	d	$c + d =$	75
		$a + c = 50$	$b + d = 100$	$N =$	150

Case 2 *Conditional Association*

	Aggressor	Non-aggressor	
Attacked	50	25	75
Not attacked	0	75	75
	50	100	150

Case 3 *Perfect Association*

	Aggressor	Non-aggressor	
Attacked	50	0	50
Not attacked	0	100	100
	50	100	150

Case 4 *Independence*

	Aggressor	Non-aggressor	
Attacked	25	50	75
Not attacked	25	50	75
	50	100	150

Case 5 *Imperfect Association*

	Aggressor	Non-aggressor	
Attacked	40	35	75
Not attacked	10	65	75
	50	100	150

cell entries have been symbolized from left to right, up and then down, by *a*, *b*, *c*, and *d*. *N*, the total number of cell entries, equals $a + b + c + d$. It should be clear that, once any *one* of these cells is determined, all the rest of them can be filled in from a knowledge of the marginal distributions.

What cell entries are possible if Aristotle's generalization is correct? Two plausible answers, Cases 2 and 3, are presented in Table 4.1. The *conditional* interpretation suggests *if* a state wrongly aggresses, *then* it will be attacked. Using the cell entry specifications given in Case 1, the conditional interpretation of Aristotle's hypothesis means that *a* will equal 50, because all 50 aggressors are attacked. Other Case-2 cell entries have been determined by subtraction. Seventy-five non-aggressors have avoided being attacked; twenty-five states, however, have been attacked, even though they have not (wrongly) aggressed (refer to Table 4.1 on page 57).

In addition to saying that wrong aggression was a *sufficient* condition for being attacked, Aristotle might have wanted to assert that wrong aggression was also a *necessary* condition for being attacked, i.e., that no one was attacked who had not previously committed un-provoked aggression. This would mean in effect that aggression was a necessary and sufficient condition for attack to occur.[2] In this hy-pothetical situation (Case 3) there would be no off-diagonal entries. (Note that the frequencies in the margins, called marginal distributions, would have to change from those in Case 2 for this to be possible.) Such a relation between attributes may be called complete or *perfect association*.

What would the cell entries be if there were no relationship between attributes? Yule, a modern statistician, argues as follows:

If there is no sort of relationship of any kind between two attributes *A* and *B*, we expect to find the same proportion of *B*'s amongst the *A*'s as amongst the not-*A*'s.[3]

He defines unrelated attributes as independent, and states as a *criterion of independence* the relationship

$$\frac{a}{a + c} = \frac{b}{b + d} = \frac{a + b}{N} \tag{4.1}$$

[2] Modern logicians define a necessary and sufficient relationship between sen-tences *p* and *q* with an equivalence sign ($\equiv$). The equivalence relation holds if and only if both the conditionals $p \supset q$ and $q \supset p$ are true:

$$(p \equiv q) \equiv [(p \supset q) \cdot (q \supset p)]$$

[3] G. Udney Yule and M. G. Kendall, *An Introduction to the Theory of Statistics* (New York: Hafner Publishing Company, 1954), p. 25 ff.

Given fixed marginal distributions, such as $a + c$ and $a + b$, what would we expect a to equal under the assumption of independence? Using the first and last terms in Equation (4.1), the expected value of a if no relationship exists (denoted a_0) is

$$a_0 = \frac{a + c}{N} \cdot \frac{a + b}{N} \cdot N = \frac{(a + c)(a + b)}{N} \qquad (4.2)$$

Equation (4.2) shows that assuming the independence of dichotomous attributes implies that any cell in a 2×2 table can be obtained by multiplying the two relevant marginal proportions by the total population size. For example, in Case 4 of Table 4.1 assuming that the marginals are fixed and represent unrelated attributes implies that the cells on the left should have frequencies of $75/150 \cdot 50/150 \cdot 150$, which equals 25. Similarly, the cells on the right of Case 4 should contain $75/150 \cdot 100/150 \cdot 150$, or 50 city-states.

COEFFICIENTS OF ASSOCIATION BETWEEN ATTRIBUTES. What happens if, as in Case 5 of Table 4.1, there is no longer a perfect relationship, nor even a conditional association, between attributes A and B? Aristotle tried to deal with *imperfect association* by introducing involved "modal" predicates like "it is possible that," "it is not necessary that not," and so on. Modern statisticians have taken another tack, and concentrated on defining and making sense of the *degree* to which the relationship between two attributes differs from what would be expected in the case of independence. Many of the measures that have been developed get fairly complicated for larger sized contingency tables; fortunately, definitions of measures of association for the 2×2 table are often closely related and quite easy to calculate.

1. *Differences in Proportions.* It makes good sense to describe both the direction and the extent of association between attributes in terms of departures from independence. Yule's criterion of independence, in terms of Table 4.1, was that the proportion of aggressors attacked should equal the proportion of non-aggressors attacked. Differences in proportions are usually identified by the Greek symbol ϵ ("epsilon") and, by some convention, are assumed to result from subtracting proportions in a certain order. Using the proportions in Equation (4.1) in the order given there,

$$\epsilon = \frac{a}{a + c} - \frac{b}{b + d} = \frac{ab + ad - ab - bc}{(a + c)(b + d)} = \frac{ad - bc}{(a + c)(b + d)} \qquad (4.3)$$

Other differences, like those comparing the proportions of a's to c's, could also be calculated in a similar manner.

2. *Differences between Observed and Marginally Expected Cell Entries.* The derivative form of the criterion of independence in Equation (4.2) also suggests a frequently used measure of association. Why not measure the *extent* to which each cell in a contingency table departs from what it would be in the case of independence between the attributes *A* and *B*? For instance, using a zero subscript to refer to expected cell frequencies, calculated only from the marginals, Yule defines a measure δ_a (read "delta-sub-*a*") equal to the difference between *a* and a_0:

$$\delta_a = a - a_0 = a - \frac{(a + b)(a + c)}{N} \tag{4.4}$$

As was pointed out earlier, there is only one choice left in assigning cell entries, once marginals are fixed. The measure δ_a succeeds in capturing this single degree of freedom. Therefore, we can show that *in the 2 $\times$ 2 contingency table, δ's are everywhere the same, except for their signs.* The proof of this result is suggested by the following way of rewriting a 2 $\times$ 2 contingency table:

	B present	*B* absent	
A present	$a_0 + \delta_a$	$b_0 + \delta_b$	$a + b$
A absent	$c_0 + \delta_c$	$d_0 + \delta_d$	$c + d$
	$a + c$	$b + d$	N

In this table each cell frequency is expressed as the sum of its marginally expected entry and its δ. The way to show that any two δ's in a row or column are equal to each other, with opposite signs, is to prove that the expected entries sum to the related marginals, in which case the relevant δ's must sum to zero. Thus, for example, if $a_0 + b_0 = a + b$, then δ_a must $= -\delta_b$. That this and other similar relations are true follows simply from the definitions of expected cell entries given above. In our example,

$$
\begin{aligned}
a_0 + b_0 &= \frac{(a + c)(a + b)}{N} + \frac{(a + b)(b + d)}{N} \\
&= \frac{a^2 + ac + ab + bc + ab + b^2 + ad + bd}{N} \\
&= \frac{a(a + c + b + d) + b(c + a + b + d)}{N} \\
&= \frac{N(a + b)}{N} \\
&= a + b \tag{4.5}
\end{aligned}
$$

Because, after ignoring signs, the δ's are the same for each cell in a 2×2 table, any one of them gives a simply interpretable measure of association. Therefore we can hereafter omit the subscript of δ_a when its meaning is clear.

3. *The Cross-Product between A and B.* Recall the configuration of a, b, c, and d introduced in Table 4.1. High a's and d's correspond to a strong association between attributes A and B. One way of measuring the degree to which cells a and d are large while b and c are small is to subtract their respective products. The resulting expression, $ad - bc$, is called a cross-product because it results from subtracting products along the two sides of a cross:

Cross-products for proportions are also easy to define. Let proportions be denoted by subscripted P's:

$$P_a = \frac{a}{N}, \qquad P_b = \frac{b}{N}, \qquad P_{a+b} = \frac{a+b}{N} \qquad (4.6)$$

Similarly the cross-product between attributes A and B, C_{AB}, can be defined as

$$C_{AB} = P_a P_d - P_b P_c \qquad (4.7)$$

Expressing the proportions according to their definitions [as indicated in Equation (4.6)],

$$C_{AB} = \frac{ad}{N^2} - \frac{bc}{N^2} = \frac{1}{N^2}(ad - bc) \qquad (4.8)$$

A surprising property of the cross-product C_{AB} is that it is just an average δ, an average difference between observed and marginally expected cell entries in a 2×2 table. This result, which is easy to derive, means that cross-products, as well as ϵ's and δ's, measure departures from the criterion of independence! In establishing this relationship it is convenient to redefine C_{AB} and show its equivalence to the cross-product formula in Equation (4.8) above. Therefore let us say that

$$C_{AB} = P_a - (P_a)_0 \qquad (4.9)$$

where $(P_a)_0$ is the proportion of a's that are expected to occur when

A and *B* are independent. $(P_a)_0$, which is just a_0 divided by N, can be calculated from table marginals. Thus, using Equation (4.2),

$$C_{AB} = \frac{a}{N} - \frac{a_0}{N} = \frac{a}{N} - \frac{(a+c)(a+b)}{N^2}$$

Since N equals $a + b + c + d$, this expression can be rewritten and simplified as

$$
\begin{aligned}
C_{AB} &= \frac{1}{N^2} [aN - (a+b)(a+c)] \\
&= \frac{1}{N^2} (a^2 + ab + ac + ad - a^2 - ab - ac - bc) \\
&= \frac{1}{N^2} (ad - bc) \qquad\qquad (4.10) \\
&= \frac{\delta}{N}
\end{aligned}
$$

Taken together with Equation (4.3), the result in Equation (4.10) shows that ϵ, δ, and C_{AB} all have simple cross-product terms $(ad - bc)$ in their numerators and are thus both computationally and conceptually related.

4. *Chi-Square* (χ^2) *and Phi-Square* (ϕ^2). Two other measures of association, frequently found in the statistical literature, are χ^2 and ϕ^2.[4] Because ϕ^2 is defined as χ^2 divided by N, it will be sufficient to describe χ^2's construction and refer to ϕ^2 as an average χ^2. χ^2 can be defined in terms of the δ's discussed above. Basically, for each cell in a contingency table, it sums the ratio

$$\frac{(\text{Observed frequency} - \text{Expected frequency})^2}{\text{Expected frequency}}.$$

χ^2 numerators are squared so that positive and negative deviations do

[4] The most serious omission from this brief list of coefficients of association for 2×2 tables is Yule's Q:

$$Q = \frac{N\delta}{ad + bc}$$

Unlike ϵ, δ, and C_{AB}, it ranges from -1 to $+1$ and does not depend for its value on changes in the marginals. For an extended and easy to follow account of these and other measures of association, particularly when they are generalized to 2×3, 3×3, etc., tables, see Morris Zelditch, Jr., *A Basic Course in Sociological Statistics* (New York: Holt, Rinehart and Winston, 1959), Chapters 6 and 7.

not cancel each other out. Letting E_i refer to marginally expected cell entries (zero subscripts are a clumsy notation for this definition):

$$\chi^2 = \sum_{i=1}^{\text{\# of cells}} \frac{\delta_i^2}{E_i} \tag{4.11}$$

and

$$\phi^2 = \chi^2/N \tag{4.12}$$

Computational formulas for these measures are given in Table 4.2. It is immediately clear that both χ^2 and ϕ^2 also have cross-product terms in the numerators, although, unlike the measures discussed above, these are squared. The really basic dissimilarity between χ^2, ϕ^2, and the earlier measures is in their denominators. The difference in proportions coefficient ϵ has a product of two marginals in its denominator, while χ^2 and ϕ^2 have all four. Both δ and C_{AB} use N or N^2 as rough equivalents for these alternatives. If all marginals were equal, ϵ, C_{AB}, and ϕ (not ϕ^2) would all have N^2 terms in their denominators; δ and χ (not χ^2) would only use denominators of N. Later in this chapter, we shall use the numerator and denominator similarities to show a systematic correspondence between these measures of *attribute* association and the standard ways of correlating *interval* scales!

Table 4.2. **Five measures of association in 2×2 contingency tables.**

1. $\epsilon = \dfrac{a}{a+c} - \dfrac{b}{b+d} = \dfrac{ad-bc}{(a+c)(b+d)}$

2. $\delta_a = a - a_0 = a - \dfrac{(a+b)(a+c)}{N} = \dfrac{ad-bc}{N}$

3. $C_{AB} = P_aP_d - P_bP_c = P_a - (P_a)_0 = \dfrac{ad-bc}{N^2}$

4. $\chi^2 = \displaystyle\sum_{i=1}^{\text{\# of cells}} \dfrac{\delta_i^2}{E_i} = \dfrac{N(ad-bc)^2}{(a+c)(b+d)(a+b)(c+d)}$

5. $\phi^2 = \dfrac{\chi^2}{N} = \dfrac{(ad-bc)^2}{(a+c)(b+d)(a+b)(c+d)}$

Notes: a, b, c, d, and N have meanings as assigned in Table 4.1; P's refer to proportions of N in a particular cell or margin; zero subscripts (as in a_0) refer to marginally expected cell frequencies; so does E_i, which equals $N \cdot (P_i)_0$.

SOME EXAMPLE CALCULATIONS. Since this book is intended as an intellectual stimulant rather than a statistical cookbook, the discussion of measures of attribute association has focused on their substantive content. But statistical formulas are rarely appreciated until they have been used. Therefore, let us test Aristotle's hypothesis, that attacks on Greek city-states could be explained by unprovoked aggressions, against the hypothetical data of Case 5 in Table 4.1.

1. The coefficient ϵ gives the proportion of aggressors attacked minus the proportion of non-aggressors that were attacked:

$$\epsilon = \frac{40}{50} - \frac{35}{100} = \frac{45}{100} = \frac{9}{20}$$

"History" indicates that Aristotle was right to the extent that aggressors have a 45 percent greater chance of being attacked than non-aggressors. Applying the same procedure to the case of conditional association in Table 4.1 reveals that the marginals given there restrict ϵ to a maximum of 0.67. The results of this and other calculations for the cases of imperfect, conditional, and perfect association are summarized in Table 4.3.

2. To calculate δ, find the difference between the actual and the marginally expected entry in a single cell. If attributes A and B are independent of each other, the expected frequency a_0 is proportional to the appropriate marginal product:

$$a_0 = \frac{75}{150} \cdot \frac{50}{150} \cdot 150 = \frac{1}{2} \cdot \frac{1}{3} \cdot 150 = 25$$

Therefore $\delta = 40 - 25 = 15$. For the table in Case 5 of Table 4.1 it can be said that there are 15 more attacked aggressors than would occur if (prior) aggressiveness could not be used to explain the number of attacks on city-states.

3. The cross-product C_{AB} was shown above to be the deviation of cell proportions from their marginally expected values, or what amounted to an average δ. Using the latter approach for computational simplicity, it is clear that C_{AB} is just 15/150, or 0.10. The 15-unit deviation mentioned above indicates that each cell in the 2×2 contingency table contains 10 percent more or less city-states than would be true in the case of independence between aggression and being attacked.

4. Chi-square and phi-square may again be discussed together. Dividing δ^2 by various marginally expected cell entries gives

$$\chi^2 = \frac{15^2}{25} + \frac{15^2}{25} + \frac{15^2}{50} + \frac{15^2}{50} = 9 + 9 + 4\tfrac{1}{2} + 4\tfrac{1}{2} = 27$$

Using the cross-product formula in Table 4.2 also gives the same result:

$$\chi^2 = \frac{150(40 \cdot 65 - 35 \cdot 10)^2}{75 \cdot 75 \cdot 50 \cdot 100} = 27$$

Finally, $\phi^2 = 27/150$ or 0.18. Computing ϕ^2 for the strongest possible conditional association with the same marginals gives 0.50, so that ϕ^2 appears to have reached 36 percent of its maximum value.[5]

Table 4.3. **Six measures of attribute association applied to hypothetical relationships between wrong aggression and being attacked.**

	Coefficient	Case 5: Imperfect Association	Case 2: Conditional Association	Case 3: Perfect Association	Comment
1.	ϵ	0.45	0.67	1	Maximum is 1 if marginals allow
2.	δ	15	25	$33\frac{1}{3}$	
3.	C_{AB}	0.10	0.17	0.22	Maximum value with equal marginals is $\frac{1}{4}$
4.	χ^2	27	75	150	
5.	ϕ^2	0.18	0.50	1	
6.	Yule's Q	0.37	1	1	Equates conditional and perfect association

Notes: Data for these calculations are taken from Table 4.1. All coefficient definitions except Yule's Q (see footnote 4) are summarized in Table 4.2. In each case, the coefficient is for a hypothetical universe of 150 Greek city-states.

B. Correlation and Regression Analysis

Statisticians have proliferated imaginative measures of association between qualitative attributes. As ways of testing or reformulating hypotheses they allow specific, if somewhat diverse, interpretations. Fortunately, statisticians show a much greater degree of unanimity as to ways of stating and testing for relationships between quantitative variables. For interval or ratio scales an elaborate and impressive set of correlational tools is available. Correlation and regression analysis can also be explored for insights into the meaning of the various qualitative measures of association that have already been discussed.

VOTING AND GOVERNMENT SPENDING. It will be easier to work with a specific example. Using data on as many countries as possible, let us

[5] Yule's Q is

$$Q = \frac{150 \cdot 15}{40 \cdot 65 + 10 \cdot 35} = \frac{1}{3}$$

This measure has the attractive property of equalling unity for both conditional and perfect associations. For measuring sufficient conditions it can be very useful.

test the hypothesis that higher levels of political participation (the independent variable) can explain higher levels of government activity (for present purposes, the dependent variable). When there is an active public, the argument goes, it is not unreasonable to suppose that government will also be highly involved in the affairs of a nation.

The explanatory relationship between these variables will have interesting payoffs even if the hypothesis is only partly accurate. If there is some kind of general but imperfect association between these variables, it will be interesting to see if government activity in particular countries, like the United States, exceeds what *empirically* would be expected of nations with similar levels of political participation. Politically, of course, there is a great debate about whether or not government in the United States *ought* to be acting as it is. Putting the relevant relationship between these two variables into cross-national perspective will provide ammunition for at least one side of the argument.

Operationally, let us use voting levels and general government expenditures as indices, respectively, of political participation and government activity.[6] For easier and more relevant comparisons, each variable has been statistically normalized: voting levels have been divided by the voting age population, and government expenditures (including central and local government, public enterprises, and social security) have been expressed as percentages of Gross National Products. Included in the analysis were data for 26 non-Communist countries.

FREQUENCY DISTRIBUTIONS.   The first step will be to look at the frequency distributions of the independent and dependent variables. When variables can take on many more than the two values possible for dichotomous attributes, graphical methods for displaying distributions are particularly appropriate. In Figure 4.1 the bar graphs representing the number of states within the various ranges of each variable are called *histograms;* the lines joining the midpoint for each range category are called *frequency polygons.* Data have been grouped into 10 or 20 percent intervals to give a good idea of the overall shape of the frequency distributions. When these intervals are the same, *areas* of histograms are proportional to the frequencies being portrayed;

---

[6] The correlation presented here was first established cross-nationally for a large number of countries in H. R. Alker, Jr., and B. M. Russett, "Correlations between indices of political and social development," in B. M. Russett, H. R. Alker, Jr., K. W. Deutsch, H. D. Lasswell *et al., World Handbook of Political and Social Indicators* (New Haven: Yale University Press, 1964). Results using different indices of government activity are remarkably similar. Data, sources, and comments about their accuracy are included in the *Handbook.*

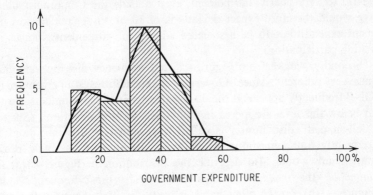

A. GOVERNMENT EXPENDITURES AS % OF G.N.P.

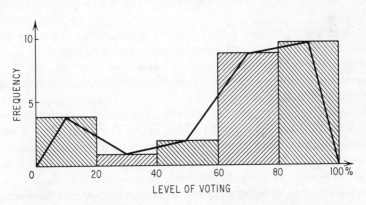

B. VOTING LEVELS AS % OF VOTING AGE POPULATION

FIGURE 4.1 Histograms and frequency polygons for government expenditures and voting participation in 26 non-Communist countries. (*Source: See note 7.*)

they can be cumulated from left to right just like the cumulative frequency distributions used in Chapter 3.

Such graphs serve two important purposes, preliminary to ascertaining relationships between two variables. First, they tell us something about the range of variation involved. Most expenditure percentages are between 10 and 50 percent; voting participation, on the other hand, ranges from 0 percent (in countries with no elections in the past 6 years) to very nearly 100 percent, even outside the Communist bloc. We would therefore expect deviations of 10 or 20 percent in government expenditures to be associated with 30 or 40 percent changes in voting participation.

Secondly, we see from Figure 4.1 that frequency distributions may have very different shapes. Government expenditures as a percentage of GNP frequently appear in the 30 to 40 percent range; numbers above or below this level are increasingly unlikely in both directions. Such a "bell-shaped" distribution is called approximately "normal" and is frequently found in statistical analysis. Because of its single peak, statisticians would also describe the distribution in Figure 4.1(a) as *unimodal*—the *mode* of a distribution is its most frequent value. Figure 4.1(b), on the other hand, is quite definitely *bimodal;* low and high voting turnouts are more frequent than medium ones. In this sense the United States, with moderate turnouts in the 50's and 60's, is somewhat atypical when compared with other non-Communist countries.

Testing Hypotheses with Regression Equations. Data on both variables may be displayed simultaneously, very much as in the case of contingency tables. Geometrical presentations, however, are particularly appropriate for quantitative relationships. Looking at the scatterplot in Figure 4.2 makes it immediately obvious that there is some kind of overall positive association between political participation and government spending. The two lines drawn there indicate that additional questions need to be answered. In particular, what is the form of the relationship between voting levels and government expenditures and how accurate is the hypothesis? Because the data do not all fit on a single line, either straight or curved, it is not obvious how best to describe the increasing effect that voting levels appear to have on government expenditures.

The simplest and most direct way of describing the actual form and accuracy of this relationship is in terms of a best fitting straight line like that in Figure 4.1. But how do we determine the best fitting line? It can be uniquely determined from the following conventions and assumptions.

1. Let $i = 1, 2, \ldots, N$ be an integer ranging from 1 to N, the number of units being studied. In the above example $N = 26$, the number of countries for which data were available. Similarly, let Y_i stand for actual expenditures and X_i the voting level of country i, Y_i's, values of the dependent variable, will be plotted on the vertical axis, while the X_i's will be horizontally arranged. Since it will be convenient to talk

about deviations above and below the average values of these variables, let

$$\overline{Y} = \frac{1}{N} \sum_{i=1}^{N} Y_i; \qquad \overline{X} = \frac{1}{N} \sum_{i=1}^{N} X_i \qquad (4.13)$$

and

$$y_i = Y_i - \overline{Y}; \qquad x_i = X_i - \overline{X} \qquad (i = 1, \ldots, N) \quad (4.14)$$

These last equations say that notationally small x's and y's are equivalent to capital X's and Y's taken about their means. Statisticians sometimes refer to the small x's and y's as "moments" of the X's and Y's, like, for example, in the definition of the "product-moment correlation coefficient" to be discussed below.

2. For the present suppose that a *linear equation* provides a satisfactory approximation to the true relationship involved. The original hypothesis, which was not specific on this point, will thus be interpreted as saying that changes in government expenditures are *proportional* to changes in voting levels. Because a linear relationship is assumed, similar changes along the X-axis should everywhere correspond to the same changes along the Y-axis. Interval scale measurement is also clearly required.

Mathematically, the linear model being introduced can be expressed in terms of the independent variable X and *predicted* value of Y, symbolized $\hat{Y}$ (read "Y-hat"):

$$\hat{Y} = a + bX \qquad (4.15)$$

If X equals 0, $\hat{Y} = a$; therefore a is known as the *Y-intercept*, the point where the line $\hat{Y} = a + bX$ intercepts the Y-axis. The coefficient b, called the *slope* of the straight line, tells how much $\hat{Y}$ changes for a unit change in X. If $b = 1/2$, for example, a 20 percent change in political participation will result in only a $1/2(20) = 10$ percent change in government activity.

The problem is now reduced to finding and commenting on the values of a and b for the best fitting linear relationship. This line will be called the *regression line*, its equation will be referred to as the *regression equation*, and b will be named the *regression coefficient*.[7]

---

[7] Using the term *regression* for these purposes is an established convention, even though its verbal significance is no longer clear. It was introduced by Galton, an English biologist in the nineteenth century, known for his work on genius and heredity. "Galton found that the sons of fathers who deviate x inches from the mean height of all fathers themselves deviate from the mean height of all sons by less than x inches; i.e., there is what Galton called a 'regression to mediocracy'." In other words, the regression coefficient b for the relationship was less than 1, but greater than zero. Yule and Kendall, *op. cit.*, p. 207.

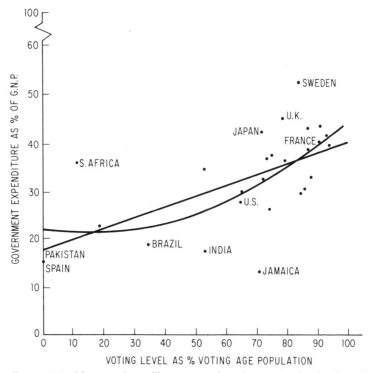

FIGURE 4.2   Linear and curvilinear regressions between voting levels and government expenditures ($N = 26$). (*Source: See note 7.*)

Too few political scientists realize that the statistician calculates the a and b of a regression equation only *after* the data have been collected. Thus $\hat{Y}$'s might more accurately be described as "postdicted" rather than "predicted." There is no certainty that regression equations calculated for one year will hold the next. We shall nonetheless conform to the ordinary practice of using "prediction" when "postdiction" might be more appropriate.

3. Criteria for establishing the best fitting straight line for the scatter-plot in Figure 4.2 must now be established. Only two of these need to be stated; reasoning from them leads to unique values of a and b. What seem like appropriate criteria? First, the line going through these points obviously should not be too high or too low. In other words, a reasonable requirement is that average deviations of actual data from the regression line should be zero. Formally, using i's as sub-scripts referring to individual nations, define $d_i = Y_i - \hat{Y}_i$ as the

deviation between the actual expenditure level Y_i and the expenditure level $\hat{Y}_i$ predicted by the best fitting linear equation. (The reader may refer to this last symbol either as "Y-hat-sub-i" or "Y-sub-i-hat!") The criterion of average or total deviations being zero can then be expressed as in Equation (4.16):

$$\sum_{i=1}^{N} d_i = \sum_{i=1}^{N} (Y_i - \hat{Y}_i) = \sum_{i=1}^{N} (Y_i - a - bX_i) = 0 \qquad (4.16)$$

All forms of this equation are equivalent because of the definitions of d_i and Y_i.

From this criterion alone it is possible to find one equation relating a and b and one point on the best fitting line! Summing the terms in the last part of Equation (4.16),

$$\sum_{i=1}^{N} Y_i - \sum_{i=1}^{N} a - \sum_{i=1}^{N} bX_i = 0$$

Constants like a and b can be moved outside of a summation sign, leaving 1's behind. Summing 1's gives N, so that

$$\sum_{i=1}^{N} Y_i - a \cdot N - b \sum_{i=1}^{N} X_i = 0$$

Dividing by N and keeping only a on the left of the equation,

$$a = \frac{1}{N} \sum_{i=1}^{N} Y_i - \frac{b}{N} \sum_{i=1}^{N} X_i$$

or

$$a = \overline{Y} - b\overline{X} \qquad (4.17)$$

Going back to the equation of the best fitting line (4.15), and substituting this expression for a,

$$\hat{Y} = \overline{Y} - b\overline{X} + bX$$

or

$$\hat{Y} - \overline{Y} = b(X - \overline{X})$$

Defining $\hat{y}$ as $\hat{Y} - \overline{Y}$ and substituting $\hat{y}$ and x for their equivalent expressions, we see that this equation becomes Equation (4.18):

$$\hat{y} = bx \qquad (4.18)$$

Equation (4.18) tells us that when $x = 0$ (i.e., X takes on its average value), so must $\hat{y}$. Therefore the best fitting line must pass through the point at which both X and $\hat{Y}$ take on their average value. Such a finding is not obvious in the earlier assumption that the average deviation should be zero, but it certainly is consonant with it and intuitively satisfying.

4. Finally, one more criterion is needed to establish the coefficients of the best fitting linear equation. We already know that the regression line is somewhere in the "middle" of the scatter diagram, but do not yet know anything about its slope. A unique value of b should be discoverable if another restriction is imposed on the d_i already used above. One such approach would be to minimize the average *absolute value* of the d_i (i.e., ignore their signs). It has become the practice, however, to find the values of a and b that minimize *squared* deviations from the regression line; in effect, extreme deviations are doubly guarded against. Symbolically this "least-squares" criterion requires that

$$\sum_{i=1}^{N} d_i^2 = \sum_{i=1}^{N} (Y_i - a - bX_i)^2 = \text{a minimum} \qquad (4.19)$$

The solution to minimization and maximization problems requires a minimal knowledge of the calculus and will have to be taken on faith, unless the reader can follow the derivation appended below.[8]

To summarize the results, Equations (4.20) give us a deductive mathematical solution to the problem of finding the best fitting linear relationship between government expenses and voting participation.

---

[8] Substituting the definition of $\hat{Y}_i$ into the definition of d_i,

$$d_i = (Y_i - \hat{Y}) = (Y_i - a - bX_i)$$

Using the value of a calculated in Equation (4.17) above,

$$d_i = (Y_i - \overline{Y} + b\overline{X} - bX_i) = y_i - bx_i$$

Our task is to minimize an expression, call it D, of the form

$$D = \sum d_i^2 = \sum (y_i - bx_i)^2 = \sum y_i^2 - 2b\sum x_i y_i + b^2 \sum x_i^2$$

and solve for b. The calculus finds maximum or minimum values of b at the points where the rate of change of D with respect to b is 0. It also requires (as is the case here) that dD/db be positive nearby minimizing values of b. This rate of change dD/db is found by a technique known as differentiation:

$$\frac{dD}{db} = -2\sum x_i y_i + 2b\sum x_i^2$$

Setting the derivative equal to zero, we find that

$$b = \frac{\sum x_i y_i}{\sum x_i^2}$$

Given the assumptions discussed in paragraphs numbered 1 to 4 above,

$$b = \frac{\sum x_i y_i}{\sum x_i^2}$$

$$a = \overline{Y} - b\overline{X}$$

(4.20)

Actually calculating the values of a and b for the regression equation of Figure 4.2 shows that

$$\hat{Y}_i = 16 + 0.27 X_i$$ (4.21)

According to the original hypothesis, government expenditures can, to some extent, be explained by popular political participation. Assuming (or hypothesizing) a linear relationship allows us to say much more: the best general estimates of expenditures can be obtained by starting with a minimum value of 16 percent and adding 0.27 times a nation's percentage voting participation.

Like the original hypothesis, Equation (4.21) is really a simple theory for explaining government expenditures. It might be applied to other data and individual nations' over time. Its accuracy, however, is not perfect, even for the data at hand. Consider, for example, the United States, with national voting levels around 64 percent. The theory predicts it will have government expenditures equal to $16 + 0.27(64.4) = 33$ percent of its GNP, about 5 percent higher than it actually has. Empirically, this result is not too different from the actual expenditure level, considering the simplicity of the regression model. In the related political and moral controversy, this finding can be interpreted in several ways. From one point of view, the United States is 5 percent "below par" in its government expenditures. Some conservatives, on the other hand, might argue that the trend in other parts of the non-Communist world is higher than it should be.

THE STRENGTH AND ACCURACY OF LINEAR RELATIONSHIPS. How accurate is this model in predicting government expenditures from voting levels? How closely does the regression equation fit the actual data of the scatter diagram? How much of the variability in Y has been explained? These questions can conveniently be answered in terms of the sum of squared deviations from the regression line that was minimized in the "least-squares" analysis. A theorist would hope, for example, that squared deviations from the regression line for his hypothesis would be a lot smaller than squared deviations in the dependent variable before the regression line was taken into account.

Statisticians have defined the *variance* of a variable as its average squared deviation about its mean. The total variance of a variable (symbolized by s^2) can be broken up into explained and unexplained parts. Symbolically, the total variance of Y (denoted s_Y^2 or, equivalently, s_y^2) is:

$$\text{Total variance} = s_Y^2 = \frac{1}{N} \sum_{i=1}^{N} (Y_i - \overline{Y})^2 = \frac{1}{N} \sum_{i=1}^{N} y_i^2 \qquad (4.22)$$

We know that the regression equation failed to explain differences between actual Y_i's and predicted Y_i's. The "unexplained variance" (s_d^2) is just the average sum of squared deviations from the predictions of the regression model:

$$\text{Unexplained variance} = s_d^2 = \frac{1}{N} \sum_{i=1}^{N} d_i^2 = \frac{1}{N} \sum_{i=1}^{N} (Y_i - \hat{Y}_i)^2$$
$$(4.23)$$

After labeling squared deviations from an average Y or predicted Y's as "total" and "unexplained" variances respectively, the only other possible difference, between predicted Y's and average Y's, must indicate the amount of Y actually *explained* by the regression model. Squaring this difference,

$$\text{Explained variance} = s_{\hat{Y}-\overline{Y}}^2 = \frac{1}{N} \sum_{i=1}^{N} (\hat{Y}_i - \overline{Y}_i)^2 \qquad (4.24)$$

The bigger the explained variance, the closer in size it is to the total variance, and the smaller the amount of unexplained deviations. The mathematical identity between these component parts of the total variance is:[9]

$$\underbrace{\frac{1}{N} \sum_{i=1}^{N} (Y_i - \overline{Y})^2}_{\text{Total variance}} = \underbrace{\frac{1}{N} \sum_{i=1}^{N} (\hat{Y}_i - \overline{Y}_i)^2}_{\text{Explained variance}} + \underbrace{\frac{1}{N} \sum_{i=1}^{N} (Y_i - \hat{Y}_i)^2}_{\text{Unexplained variance}}$$
$$(4.25)$$

[9] This equation can be proved from the simple tautology

$$\underbrace{Y_i - \overline{Y}}_{\substack{\text{Total devi-}\\\text{ation}}} = \underbrace{(Y_i - \hat{Y}_i)}_{\substack{\text{Unexplained}\\\text{deviation}}} + \underbrace{(\hat{Y}_i - \overline{Y})}_{\substack{\text{Explained}\\\text{deviation}}}$$

Squaring both sides of this expression,

$$\sum(Y_i - \overline{Y})^2 = \sum(Y_i - \hat{Y}_i)^2 + \sum(\hat{Y}_i - \overline{Y})^2 + 2\sum(Y_i - \hat{Y}_i)(\hat{Y}_i - \overline{Y})$$

Because $\hat{Y}_i - \overline{Y}_i = bx_i$ and $Y_i - \hat{Y}_i = y_i - bx_i$, the last term becomes $\sum(y_i - bx_i)(bx_i)$, which equals $b(\sum y_i x_i - b\sum x_i^2)$. This in turn equals zero because $b = \sum x_i y_i / \sum x_i^2$. The reader is urged to work out the details of this proof for himself, paying particular attention to the differences between capital and small letters.

With these few intellectual tools, we are able to measure the strength and the accuracy of a regression model. The strength of a regression model may be defined as the proportion of variance in the dependent variable explained by the independent variable. The result is called the coefficient of determination:

The coefficient of determination $(r^2) = \dfrac{\text{explained variance}}{\text{total variance}}$

Symbolically, this coefficient is represented by r^2. Using the definitions given above,

$$r^2 = \frac{s^2_{\hat{Y}-\overline{Y}}}{s^2_Y} = \frac{\sum(\hat{Y}_i - \overline{Y})^2}{\sum(Y_i - \overline{Y})^2} \qquad (4.26)$$

Because of its clear interpretation in terms of "the proportion of variance explained," the coefficient of determination r^2 is at least as useful as its square root, the product-moment correlation coefficient r.

It is customary to measure the accuracy of a regression model by referring to the reduction in deviations of the dependent variable brought about by use of the regression equation. Mathematically, the increased accuracy in estimating Y can be measured using square roots of the variances s^2_Y and s^2_d defined above. The basic relation between these two deviations follows easily from Equations (4.25) and (4.26):

$$\frac{s^2_d}{s^2_Y} = \frac{s^2_Y - s^2_{\hat{Y}-\overline{Y}}}{s^2_Y} = 1 - r^2 \qquad (4.27)$$

Taking square roots of the above equation, we have

$$s_d = \sqrt{1 - r^2} s_Y \qquad (4.28)$$

Both variance square roots s_d and s_Y are known as *standard deviations;* they indicate the value of the square root of the average squared deviations of d_i and Y_i, respectively. Equation (4.28) shows just exactly what proportion of the standard deviation of Y remains in the standard deviation about the regression line. The coefficient $1 - r^2$ is usually referred to as the *coefficient of alienation.*

In the government spending example pictured above, $r = +0.63$, and the coefficient of determination (r^2) is 0.40; therefore the coefficient of alienation is 0.60, with a positive square root of 0.77. As a result we can say that the simple regression model in Equation (4.15) explains 40 percent of the variance in government expenditures. Using this model thus helps predict expenditures with considerably more accuracy than we could have without it. Specifically, the standard deviation in Y can be reduced to around three-quarters of its original value, using knowledge of national voting levels. Although these findings, like any statistical analyses, make only a partial and preliminary contribution toward explaining expenditure levels, their precise meanings and attractive statistical properties are a great improvement on the "more or less associated" description that the untutored intuition might suggest.

MEANINGS OF THE CORRELATION COEFFICIENT.   The squared correlation coefficient r^2 was defined above as that fraction of the variance of Y explained by a linear regression equation in X. As such it varied between 0 and 1. This interpretation of r^2 in terms of the "fraction of variance explained" is frequently cited by political scientists who are unaware of several other equally useful equivalent definitions or interpretations. Two of these are given below.

Consider the problem of measuring associated variations in X and Y. If for country i, variables X_i and Y_i were both above average, their differences from their means (x_i and y_i) would both be above zero. Those instances when x and y were both above zero or both below zero would seem to indicate that X and Y were positively related. Those cases when one variable was above average, and the other was not, however, would indicate covariation in opposite directions. More positive and large $x_i y_i$ products than negative ones would indicate a positive association between the variables X and Y. With this rationale it is possible to define the covariation of X and Y as a sum of products of x's and y's:

$$\text{Covariation of } X \text{ and } Y = \sum_{i=1}^{N} x_i y_i \qquad (4.29)$$

The *covariance* of X and Y is the average *covariation*. It averages cross-product terms in a manner similar to the cross-product C_{AB} defined previously for dichotomous attributes:

$$\text{Covariance of } X \text{ and } Y = \frac{1}{N} \sum_{i=1}^{N} x_i y_i \qquad (4.30)$$

As we saw in Figure 4.1, however, some variables have greater ranges than others; voting percentages ranged from 0 to nearly 100 percent while government expenditures only appear to vary from about 20 to 60 percent. For empirical analysis, some standardization is required so that each variable contributes equivalent amounts to the product terms in the covariance expression. Since equal ranges of variability in X_i and Y_i cannot be assumed, it is necessary to standardize these variables by expressing them as differences about their means and then dividing them by some measure of their overall variability, e.g., their standard deviations. The variables transformed in this manner are known as *standard scores* and are usually written with the letter Z:

$$Z_x(i) = \frac{X_i - \overline{X}}{s_x}; \qquad Z_Y(i) = \frac{Y_i - \overline{Y}}{s_y} \qquad (4.31)$$

(Notationally, $Z_x(i)$ is "the standard score on variable X of individual i," which may be abbreviated drastically as "Z-sub-x-of i" and should not be confused with Z of x *times i*.)

Because standard scores for X and Y have zero means and unit variances,[10] a specially convincing measure of relationship between X and Y would be the *covariance of their standard scores*. Such a measure of "correlation" would be expressed symbolically as

$$r = \frac{1}{N} \sum_{i=1}^{N} Z_x(i)Z_y(i) = \frac{1}{N} \sum_{i=1}^{N} \left(\frac{X_i - \overline{X}}{S_x}\right)\left(\frac{Y_i - \overline{Y}}{S_y}\right) \qquad (4.32)$$

It achieves a maximum value of 1 and a minimum value of -1 in these special cases when $X_i = Y_i$ or $X_i = -Y_i$, because then the terms in Equation (4.32) reduce to the positive or negative variance of a standardized variable.

The following theorem proves that the squared correlation coefficient defined in terms of "fractional variance explained" is identical to a squared "covariance of standard scores."

---

[10] As should be expected, "standard" scores have several attractive properties: their means are zero and their variances are unity. To prove these statements are true, only elementary calculations are required. For any variable X:

$$\overline{Z}_x = \frac{1}{N} \sum \frac{X_i - \overline{X}}{s_x} = \frac{1}{N \cdot s_x}\left(\sum (X_i - \overline{X})\right) = 0$$

The expression in parentheses equals zero because, as noted in Chapter 3, average and total deviations from a mean are zero. Looking at the variance of z_x:

$$s_{Z_x}^2 = \frac{1}{N} \sum (Z_x(i) - \overline{Z}_x)^2 = \frac{1}{N} \sum \left(\frac{(X_i - \overline{X})}{s_x}\right) = \frac{1}{N \cdot s_x} \sum (X_i - \overline{X})^2 = \frac{N \cdot s_x^2}{N \cdot s_x^2} = 1$$

This equation is true because variances are both *squared standard* deviations and *average squared* deviations.

Theorem 4.1 Given two variables X_i, Y_i $(i = 1, \ldots, N)$, for which a regression equation predicting Y_i from X_i has been obtained, then

$$r^2 = \frac{\sum_{i=1}^{N} (\hat{Y}_i - \overline{Y})^2}{\sum_{i=1}^{N} (Y_i - \overline{Y})^2} = \left[\frac{1}{N} \sum_{i=1}^{N} Z_x(i)Z_y(i)\right]^2 \tag{4.33}$$

*Tactics: Subjectively, the technique of proof can be easily described. The most "atypical" expression in Equation (4.33) is $(\hat{Y}_i - \overline{Y})$. Reducing it to variances or covariances should make the equality between these two definitions of r^2 easier to establish.

*Proof: From Equation (4.18) we know that

$$\hat{y}_i = \hat{Y}_i - \overline{Y} = bx_i$$

Substituting bx_i for $\hat{Y}_i - \overline{Y}$, the numerator on the left of Equation (4.33) becomes

$$\sum_{i=1}^{N} (\hat{Y}_i - \overline{Y})^2 = \sum_{i=1}^{N} (bx_i)^2 = b^2 \sum_{i=1}^{N} x_i^2 \tag{4.34}$$

Now we already know that $b = \sum x_i y_i / \sum x_i^2$; squaring this term and substituting it into (4.34) gives

$$\sum_{i=1}^{N} (\hat{Y}_i - \overline{Y})^2 = \frac{\left(\sum_{i=1}^{N} x_i y_i\right)^2}{\sum_{i=1}^{N} x_i^2} \tag{4.35}$$

Since the denominator in (4.33) is just $\sum y_i^2$, or $N \cdot s_y^2$, and $\sum x_i^2$ in (4.35) is similarly $N \cdot s_x^2$, dividing both sides of (4.35) by $N \cdot s_y^2$ gives the required result:

$$\frac{\sum_{i=1}^{N} (\hat{Y}_i - \overline{Y})^2}{\sum_{i=1}^{N} (Y_i - \overline{Y})^2} = \frac{\left(\sum_{i=1}^{N} x_i y_i\right)^2}{N \cdot s_x^2 \cdot N \cdot s_y^2} = \left(\frac{1}{N} \sum_{i=1}^{N} \frac{x_i y_i}{s_x s_y}\right)^2$$

$$= \left(\frac{1}{N} \sum_{i=1}^{N} Z_x(i) \cdot Z_y(i)\right)^2 \qquad Q.E.D.$$

The above interpretation indicates that r^2 could have been alternatively defined as a standardized covariance, rather than as a measure of the strength of relationships. One more additional interpretation (or definition) stresses how r is related to the form of a relationship. Manipulating the formula for the slope b leads to the result that r is the *slope of a linear regression between standardized variables.* Equation (4.36) states the general relationship of which this result is a special case:[11]

$$r = b_{yx} \frac{s_x}{s_y} \qquad (4.36)$$

SUMMARY. Given two variables Y_i and X_i measured on interval or ratio scales, and unimodally or bimodally distributed, mathematicians have suggested a variety of ways of measuring *how Y* depends on X.[12] Political scientists, however, have often failed to take advantage of these various possibilities. Any relationship between two variables, for example, can be characterized as to its *form*, its *strength*, its *accuracy*, and its statistical *significance*.

The form of many relationships between political variables can be expressed by a linear regression equation; the strength or explanatory power of this relationship, measured by the coefficient of determination (r^2), tells how much variance in the dependent variables has been explained. (In the spending example, for instance, fitting the curvilinear regression in Figure 4.2 only raised r^2 from 0.58 to 0.62.) The accuracy in estimating the dependent variable in a regression equation is meas-

---

[11] The subscript on b_{yx} indicates that the dependent variable Y is being "regressed" on X. Equation (4.36) follows from definitions of the three quantities involved:

$$b_{yx} \cdot \frac{s_x}{s_y} = \frac{\sum x_i y_i}{\sum x_i^2} \cdot \frac{\sqrt{\dfrac{\sum x_i^2}{N}}}{\sqrt{\dfrac{\sum y_i^2}{N}}} = \frac{\sum x_i y_i}{\sqrt{\sum x_i^2 \sum y_i^2}} = r$$

Throughout this chapter Y (or y) has been assumed to be the "dependent" variable being explained; it is also possible, however, to reverse this assumption and regress X on Y, giving

$$b_{xy} = \frac{\sum x_i y_i}{\sum y_i^2}$$

Multiplying the formulas for these slopes (which are different unless X and Y have equal variances) gives another attractive result:

$$r^2 = b_{xy} b_{yx}$$

which in turn suggests that r^2 can also be interpreted as the product of the slope of Y regressed on X times the slope of X regressed on Y!

[12] When the frequency distributions for two variables have very different shapes, perfectly fitting linear regression equations are not possible. Transforming one or both variables until they have approximately normal distributions will sometimes improve the fit of a linear regression. The reader may like to experiment with the following transformations of X: rank of X, logarithm of X, $\sqrt{X}$ and X^2. For further sources on transformations see the literature cited at the conclusion of Chapter 2.

ured by the coefficient of alienation, the square root of which measures the decrease in the standard deviation of Y made possible by the regression equation.

The product-moment correlation coefficient r summarizes other aspects of regression analysis. Geometrically, r is the slope of the linear relationship between standardized X and Y. Algebraically, r can be formally defined as an average product or covariance of standardized variables.

C. Associating Qualities Means Correlating Quantities

It is possible to show an exact correspondence between measures introduced in the first part of this chapter for associating attributes and the various correlation coefficients just described.[13] Establishing these equivalences will

(1) show how qualitative political experiences can be quantified in a consistent way to the extent that they occur frequently and are subject to reliable and valid interpretations;

(2) indicate that techniques developed and interpreted for quantitative data suggest valuable ways of interpreting and testing political hypotheses about qualitative data;

(3) reveal one way in which mathematical reasoning can integrate a variety of ostensibly unrelated measures of statistical association, thus giving the practicing political analyst a better rationale for choosing among disparate possibilites for a particular piece of research;

(4) suggest several quick and simple ways of calculating correlation-like coefficients for 2×2 contingency tables.

CORRELATING "DUMMY VARIABLES." Returning to the examples at the beginning of this chapter, we shall quantify two attributes X_i and Y_i for N countries, $(i = 1, 2, \ldots, N)$, as follows:

> If country i is an aggressor, $X_i = 1$.
> If country i is non-aggressive, $X_i = 0$.
> If country i is attacked, $Y_i = 1$.
> If country i remains at peace, $Y_i = 0$.

The label "1" is attached to a country if and only if a certain attribute applies. The attribute can then be treated as a "dummy variable."

---

[13] The equivalences demonstrated in this section have been suggested directly or indirectly in various places. See H. M. Blalock, Jr., "A Double Standard in Measuring Degree of Association," *American Sociological Review*, **28**, 6 (December 1963), pp. 988–989; Yule and Kendall, *op. cit.*; and Lazarsfeld, "The Algebra of Dichotomous Systems," H. Solomon ed., *Studies in Item Analysis and Prediction* (Stanford: Stanford U. Press; 1961).

Such a procedure is as operational, reliable, and valid as the observer making the prior qualitative assessments. In order to add and subtract these numbers, one must talk about the *frequency* with which a certain attribute applies to the universe of states being studied. For ratio scale interpretations, it is also possible to consider X_i as the *probability* of X_i occurring, e.g., 0, 1/2, or 1.

For dichotomous, or "dummy" variables of this sort, new formulas for average values, variances, covariations, covariances, and correlations can be constructed. They may best be remembered if grouped together in the following theorem:

Theorem 4.2 For two variables X_i, Y_i $(i = 1, 2, \ldots, N)$ *taking on the values of* 1 *or* 0 *if a particular attribute is present or absent, the mean values, variances, covariations, covariances, and correlations are equivalent to the following expressions:*

Means: $$\overline{X} = P_X; \qquad \overline{Y} = P_Y \qquad (4.37a)$$

Variances: $$s_X^2 = P_X Q_X; \qquad s_Y^2 = P_Y Q_Y \qquad (4.37b)$$

Covariation of X and Y: $$\sum x_i y_i = N \cdot (P_{XY} - P_X P_Y) \qquad (4.37c)$$

Covariance of X and Y: $$\frac{1}{N} \sum x_i y_i = (P_{XY} - P_X P_Y) \qquad (4.37d)$$

Correlation of X and Y: $$\frac{1}{N} \frac{\sum x_i y_i}{s_X s_Y} = \frac{P_{XY} - P_X P_Y}{\sqrt{P_X Q_X P_Y Q_Y}} \qquad (4.37e)$$

In these expressions P_X is the proportion of cases when $X_i = 1$; similarly for P_Y. P_{XY} is the proportion of cases for which *both* X_i and $Y_i = 1$. Q_X and Q_Y, on the other hand, equal $1 - P_X$ and $1 - P_Y$, respectively; they refer to the proportions of cases in which an attribute is absent.

Tactics: Step by step, the appropriate derivations are easy to follow. All of them result from substituting new definitions of X_i and Y_i into old definitions of the various coefficients.

Proof: First, Equation (4.37a) shows that the average value of a dummy variable is equal to the proportions of cases in which the attribute occurs. Working from the definition of $\overline{X}$,

$$\overline{X} = \frac{1}{N} \sum_{i=1}^{N} X_i$$

$$= \frac{1}{N} \underbrace{(1 + 1 + 1 + \cdots + 1)}_{P_X \cdot N \text{ times}} + \frac{1}{N} \underbrace{(0 + 0 + \cdots + 0)}_{N \cdot Q_X \text{ times}} = P_X$$

Similarly, $\overline{Y} = P_Y$.

Variances are only slightly more difficult. They turn out to be products of proportions, P's times Q's. By definition, using newly derived terms for $\overline{X}$ and $\overline{Y}$,

$$s_X^2 = \frac{1}{N} \sum_{i=1}^{N} (X_i - \overline{X})^2 = \frac{1}{N} \sum_{i=1}^{N} (X_i^2 - 2P_X X_i + P_X^2)$$

But X_i is either 1 or 0, so X_i^2 always equals X_i. Summing the above expression and omitting obvious indices on the summation signs,

$$s_X^2 = \frac{\sum X_i}{N} - 2P_X \frac{\sum X_i}{N} + \frac{\sum P_X^2}{N}$$

This expression is entirely made up of proportions, so

$$s_X^2 = P_X - 2P_X^2 + P_X^2 = P_X - P_X^2 = P_X(1 - P_X) = P_X Q_X$$

It remains to derive formulas for coefficients based on covariations. Again working from previous definitions, the covariation of X and Y is

$$\sum_{i=1}^{N} (X_i - \overline{X})(Y_i - \overline{Y}) = \sum_{i=1}^{N} (X_i Y_i - \overline{X} Y_i - \overline{Y} X_i + \overline{X}\overline{Y})$$

Summing the terms in this expression will give P_X's and P_Y's in the same ways as above; adding $X_i Y_i$ products will give the number of cases in which both X_i and Y_i are non-zero. Therefore the covariation

$$= NP_{XY} - NP_X P_Y - NP_Y P_X + NP_X P_Y$$
$$= N(P_{XY} - P_X P_Y)$$

Dividing by N,

$$\text{Covariance of } X \text{ and } Y = \frac{1}{N} \sum x_i y_i = P_{XY} - P_X P_Y$$

The correlation can be found by dividing the covariance by the relevant standard deviations (variance square roots):

$$r = \frac{1}{N} \frac{\sum x_i y_i}{s_X s_Y} = \frac{P_{XY} - P_X P_Y}{\sqrt{P_X Q_X P_Y Q_Y}} \qquad \text{Q.E.D.}$$

We are now ready to show how correlational measures of association for quantitative dummy variables suggest entirely new and intellectually integrated ways of interpreting the measures of attribute association already defined and summarized in Table 4.2 near the beginning of the chapter. As a start, Equation (4.37d), giving the covariance for X and Y, has exactly the same kind of structure as the cross-product

C_{AB} in Table 4.2 on page 63. Both subtract a product of the relevant marginal proportions from the proportion of cases in the upper left-hand cell of a 2 × 2 table. (See how, notationally, P_{XY} is equivalent to P_a, and so on.) *Because the cross-product and the covariance are equivalent to each other*, we shall now use the symbol C_{XY} for either dichotomous attributes or quantified variables.

This central result establishes an exact correspondence between the cross-product numerators of a number of attribute measures of association and the product-moment numerators (summing $x_i y_i$) in measures of covariation for quantitative variables. It suggests immediately, for example, that δ_{XY} *is equivalent to the covariation between X and Y* because each is just a covariance (i.e., cross-product) multiplied by N:

$$\text{Covariation of dummy variables } X \text{ and } Y = \delta_{yx} \qquad (4.38)$$

Most of the quantitative dummy variable formulas in Theorem 4.2 had proportions and variances in their denominators. Attributes must also have similar interpretations. For attribute measures of association, let X and Y be interpreted as attributes; for quantitative correlational measures, however, consider X and Y to be the corresponding "dummy variables." (In either case Y is being explained by X.) Use a, b, c, and d to represent cell frequencies in a 2 × 2 contingency table for attributes X and Y:

		X		
		present	absent	
	present	a	b	$a + b$
Y	absent	c	d	$c + d$
		$a + c$	$b + d$	N

It follows that proportions for attributes can be expressed using a's, b's, c's, and d's; variances can then be defined as proportion products:

$$P_X = \frac{a + c}{N} \qquad\qquad Q_X = \frac{b + d}{N}$$

$$P_Y = \frac{a + b}{N} \qquad\qquad Q_Y = \frac{c + d}{N} \qquad (4.39)$$

$$s_X^2 = P_X Q_X = \frac{(a + c)(b + d)}{N^2} \qquad s_Y^2 = P_Y Q_Y = \frac{(b + d)(c + d)}{N^2}$$

Multiplying variances for X and Y gives

$$s_X^2 \cdot s_Y^2 = P_X Q_X P_Y Q_Y = \frac{(a + c)(b + d)(a + b)(c + d)}{N^4} \qquad (4.40)$$

Except for the N^4, Equation (4.40) shows that the denominator of ϕ^2 (and χ^2) in Table 4.2 is the same as that of the *squared* correlation coefficient (r^2) for dummy variables given in Theorem 4.2. Following this lead suggests trying to relate numerators for the measures of attribute association to those for dummy variable correlations. From Equation (4.7) we know that

$$C_{XY} = P_{XY} - P_X P_Y = \frac{1}{N^2}(ad - bc)$$

Squaring this expression produces the missing N^4:

$$C_{XY}^2 = \frac{(ad - bc)^2}{N^4} \tag{4.41}$$

Now, by definition, r squared for X and Y is

$$r_{XY}^2 = \frac{C_{XY}^2}{s_X^2 s_Y^2} \tag{4.42}$$

Substituting the results of (4.41) into the numerator and those of (4.40) into the denominator of Equation (4.42) indicates that

$$r_{XY}^2 = \frac{C_{XY}^2}{s_X^2 s_Y^2} = \frac{\dfrac{(ad - bc)^2}{N^4}}{\dfrac{(a + b)(c + d)(a + c)(b + d)}{N^4}}$$

$$= \frac{(ad - bc)^2}{(a + b)(c + d)(a + c)(b + d)} = \phi_{XY}^2 \tag{4.43}$$

In sum, ϕ^2 *for dichotomous attributes is equivalent to* r^2 *for dummy variables!* From this interpretation of ϕ^2 it follows that χ^2 (which by definition is $N \cdot \phi^2$) is N times the proportion of variance explained by the correlation between dummy variables based on attributes X and Y.

Of the five measures of association in Table 4.2, only one (ϵ) has not yet been reinterpreted. It is easy to show, however, that ϵ can be interpreted as the slope of a linear relationship between dichotomous variables. Rewriting the definition in Table 4.2 with X and Y notation,

$$\epsilon_{YX} = \frac{a}{a + c} - \frac{b}{b + d} = \frac{ad - bc}{(a + c)(b + d)} \tag{4.44}$$

We have shown that the covariation of X and Y is equivalent to δ, both also equaling $(ad - bc)/N$. Equations (4.39) indicate that the denominator of (4.44) equals $N^2 \cdot P_X Q_X$. Putting these reinterpretations of the numerator and denominator of Eq. (4.44) together gives

$$\epsilon_{YX} = \frac{ad - bc}{(a + c)(b + d)} = \frac{\dfrac{ad - bc}{N}}{\dfrac{(a + c)(b + d)}{N}} = \frac{\delta}{N \cdot P_X Q_X}$$

$$= \frac{\sum x_i y_i}{N \cdot s_X^2} = \frac{\sum x_i y_i}{\sum x_i^2} = b_{YX} \tag{4.45}$$

ϵ_{YX} was defined as the differences in proportions between Y's that are X's and Y's that are not X's. *For dichotomous attributes we have proved that ϵ_{YX} can be interpreted as the slope of a linear regression of Y on X.*

AN EXAMPLE. A practical consequence of the above results for political scientists is that a great many closely interrelated measures of attribute association may be given quantitative interpretations and used for a variety of special purposes in the same way that slopes, covariances, correlations, coefficients of determination, and alienation are used in regression analyses among quantitative variables. It is nonetheless true, however, that even for 2×2 tables the literature of political science often uses only χ^2 as a test of "significance," when other measures like δ, ϵ, C_{XY} or ϕ^2 would tell a good deal more about the meaning, the form, and the strength of the relationship.

Some of these possibilities will be illustrated with our earlier concrete example about the relationship between attribute $(X)_1$ committing (wrong) aggression, and attribute (Y), being attacked. The data in Figure 4.3 are taken from the earlier hypothetical example in Table 4.1. Because both variables are only dichotomies, there are but four possible combinations of X and Y values. In Figure 4.3 the number of city-states for each possibility is indicated next to a circled cross representing the X and Y values they have in common. Forty states, for example, both aggressed and were attacked during the time period being considered.

First we shall calculate regression coefficients a and b. Because $b_{YX} = \epsilon_{YX}$ the slope of the regression equation will be the proportion of aggressors attacked minus the proportion of non-aggressors attacked. From the figure we can read this difference as

$$b_{YX} = \frac{40}{50} - \frac{35}{100} = \frac{80 - 35}{100} = \frac{45}{100}$$

which corresponds to the positive relationship between X and Y previously calculated. What about a formula for the Y-intercept?

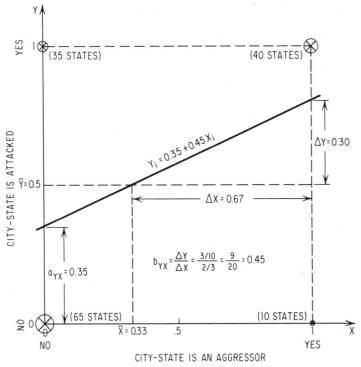

FIGURE 4.3 A regression analysis for "dummy variables" ($r_{yx} = 0.42$ $N = 150$). (*Source: See Table 4.1.*)

Recall that $a = \overline{Y} - b_{YX}\overline{X}$. In proportional terms, therefore,

$$a = P_Y - \epsilon_{YX} \cdot P_X$$

For the data at hand

$$a = \frac{50}{100} - \frac{45}{100} \cdot \frac{1}{3} = \frac{35}{100}$$

Putting these two coefficients into a linear regression model of the hypothesis being tested, we have

$$\hat{Y}_i = \frac{35}{100} + \frac{45}{100} X_i \qquad (i = 1, \ldots, 150) \qquad (4.46)$$

Plotting Equation (4.32), the Y-intercept is at 0.35; substantively, this suggests that the probability of non-aggressors' being attacked is 0.35. When $X = 1$, $\hat{Y}_i$ is $35 + 45/100 = 80/100$; again the best estimate that we can make of the chances that an aggressor will be attacked is

80 in 100. Both the slope b_{YX} and the intercept a_{YX} for the regression line through these two possibilities are illustrated in the figure; they correspond exactly to our previous calculations. And, as should also be expected, the regression line actually goes through the point at which both the Y_i and X_i achieve their average value. What is more, (4.45) suggests best predictions of Y for probabilistic values of X. When the probability that a state is an aggressor reaches $1/2$, for example, the hypothetical model in (4.46) suggests the likelihood of being attacked to be about 0.58.

What is the correlation coefficient corresponding to this regression? Lumbering through the long formulas given in Table 4.2 or Equation (4.19) would be very monotonous. Remembering from Equation (4.33) that $r = b \cdot s_X / s_Y$, however, reduces calculations considerably:

$$r = b \cdot \sqrt{\frac{P_X Q_X}{P_Y Q_Y}} = \frac{9}{20} \sqrt{\frac{\left(\frac{1}{3}\right)\left(\frac{2}{3}\right)}{\left(\frac{1}{2}\right)\left(\frac{1}{2}\right)}} = \frac{9}{20} \sqrt{\frac{8}{9}} = \frac{3}{10} \sqrt{2} = 0.42$$

$$(4.47)$$

The fact that $\sqrt{2} = 1.41$ may be remembered, calculated, or looked up in a table of square roots.

Can one use the same interpretations of r_{YX} and r_{YX}^2 offered before in the 2×2 case? Yes, if they refer to dummy variables. An r_{YX} of 0.42 in our hypothetical example tells us first that for city-states there is a positive covariance between X, aggressiveness, and Y, being themselves attacked. Their average product as standard variables is 0.42. If marginal distributions were identical, the slope of the least-squares linear relationship between these variables would also be 0.42. In fact, because Y has a more equal distribution and a slightly larger variance, the slope for untransformed variables is actually 0.45. Squaring r to get the coefficient of determination,

$$r_{YX}^2 = \phi_{YX}^2 = 0.42 \times 0.42 = 0.18$$

Again we find something that we previously did not know—that a simple proportionate change model explains only about one-fifth of the variance in whether or not a city-state is attacked.[14]

[14] Unequal marginals, in fact, insure that no perfect linear relation could be found. The strongest association for the given marginals has already been calculated (See Case 2 of Table 4.1 and Table 4.3) and was shown to be around 0.7. Thus the linear model actually accounts for $0.18/(0.7)^2$ or about 36 percent of the variance that can be linearly explained.

SUMMARY.   Definitions and convenient formulas for related qualitative and quantitative indices are given in Table 4.4.   Notations there correspond to those already given, except where subscripts have been dropped when their meaning is clear.

Table 4.4. **Equivalent measures of association and correlation for two dichotomous attributes, X and Y.**

Measures of association		Measures of correlation	
Formulas	*Interpretations*	*Formulas*	*Interpretations*
1. $\epsilon_{YX} = \dfrac{a}{a+c} - \dfrac{b}{b+d}$ $= \dfrac{ad-bc}{(a+c)(b+d)}$	Difference in proportions	$b = \dfrac{\sum x_i y_i}{\sum x_i^2}$	Slope of a regression
2. $\delta = a - a_0$ $= \dfrac{ad-bc}{N}$	Difference between actual and marginally expected cell entry	$\sum x_i y_i$	Covariation
3. $C_{XY} = P_{XY} - P_X P_Y$ $= \dfrac{ad-bc}{N^2}$	Cross-product	$C_{XY} = \dfrac{\sum x_i y_i}{N}$	Covariance
4. $\phi = \epsilon_{YX}\dfrac{P_X Q_X}{P_Y Q_Y}$, etc.	Ranges from -1 to $+1$ if marginals are equal	$r = \dfrac{C_{XY}}{s_X s_Y}$	Correlation; standardized covariance; regression slope for standardized variables
5. $\phi^2 = \chi^2/N$, etc.	χ^2 sums $\dfrac{(\text{actual-expected})^2}{\text{expected}}$	r^2	Percentage of variance explained

CHAPTER 5

Multiple Relationships

Anyone who suggests a variable explaining an additional 10% of the variance has made a contribution to political theory.

KARL DEUTSCH

BECAUSE POLITICAL PROCESSES and outcomes are unusually compli-cated, more than one explanatory factor is almost always required. Building on the correlational techniques previously defined and de-scribed, this chapter discusses ways in which additional variables may enter into political explanations. Attention is directed first toward ways of controlling for the effects of a third variable; then to a general result, the covariance theorem, which provides a model for all three variable relationships; and finally to both additive and multiplicative theories about politics.

A. The Effects of a Third Variable

Once data have been grouped into significant categories, the most common way of studying the effects of additional variables on two-variable relationships is known as cross-tabulation. Repeatedly tabu-lating associations between two variables for different categories of a third ("control") variable would be an example of such a cross-tabulation. Other, more complicated multiple relationships could be studied in a similar manner.

EXAMPLES OF CROSS-TABULATION. Consider the explanation of gov-ernment spending levels in terms of public participation in politics mentioned in Chapter 4. Economists and sociologists might argue that both of these variables can be explained by a country's level of economic and social development. They might hypothesize that the relationship between voting and spending will "wash out" or prove to be "spurious" when development is controlled for.

Because this hypothesis is plausible, we shall test the effect of de-velopment (measured by per capita GNP in 1957) on the previously established relationship. All three variables were dichotomized at or near their midpoints after a look at their frequency distributions.[1] For a universe of 26 nations, the relation between dichotomized voting levels and government expenditures is given in Table 5.1.[2]

Table 5.1. **A universal relationship between dichotomized voting levels and government expenditures.**

	X High voting levels	$\overline{X}$ Low voting levels	
Y High government expenditures	10	6	16
$\overline{Y}$ Low government expenditures	2	8	10
	12	14	$N = 26$

$$\epsilon_{YX} = 0.40; \qquad C_{YX} = 0.10; \qquad \phi_{YX} = 0.41$$

Values for ϵ, C_{YX}, and ϕ are calculated from the formulas in Table 4.4. Source: same as for Fig. 4.2.

Dividing the data for Table 5.1 into developed and underdeveloped tabulations and identifying the particular countries involved gives Table 5.2. It appears that most of the high-voting and high-spending nations are highly developed, while most of the low-voting and low-spending nations are underdeveloped, as was previously suggested.

---

[1] Data are again taken from Russett, and Alker, Deutsch, Lasswell, *World Handbook of Political and Social Indicators* (New Haven: Yale University Press, 1964). Per capita GNP in 1957 is one of a highly intercorrelated net of indices of development, all of which would give roughly the same results as are being described here. Government expenditures clustering above 31 percent have been considered "high," as have voting levels above 75 percent. The developed-underdeveloped cutting point was quite arbitrarily chosen—$700 per capita GNP. Ordinarily it would be desirable to keep the ordinal, interval, or ratio scale information supplied by those indices, but the dichotomous attribute or "dummy variable" approach has been chosen for simplicity in exposition.

[2] Compared with the linear regression in Figure 4.1, the dichotomized relationship has a higher slope (ϵ) and a smaller correlation (ϕ). In the original relationship the variance s_X^2 was considerably larger than that of s_Y^2, which is no longer true with variances calculated as PQ proportional products. This difference suggests one reason why the new slope (ϵ) is steeper. Another relevant factor, of course, is the extent to which information has been lost by grouping the data. Finally, the unequal marginals in Table 5.1 mean that ϕ could only take as a maximum value 0.73. $\phi/\phi_{\max}$ is thus $41/73 = 0.57$, quite close to the original value of $r_{YX} = 0.63$.

Table 5.2. A cross-tabulation of the impact of voting levels on government expenditures, controlling for levels of economic development. (All frequencies are in lower right-hand corners.)

C
High development

	X *High voting*	$\overline{X}$ *Low voting*	
Y Y High expenses	United Kingdom, France, New Zealand, Netherlands, Belgium, Norway, Sweden /8	Canada, Ireland, Finland /3	11
$\overline{Y}$ Low expenses	Denmark, Austria /2	USA /1	3
	10	4	14

$$\epsilon_{YXC} = 0.05; \quad C_{YXC} = 0.01; \quad \phi_{YXC} = 0.55$$

$\overline{C}$
Low development

	X *High voting*	$\overline{X}$ *Low voting*	
Y High expenses	Italy, Austria /2	Burma, Japan, South Africa /3	5
$\overline{Y}$ Low expenses	/0	Portugal, Spain, Greece, Brazil, Pakistan, India, Jamaica /7	7
	2	10	12

$$\epsilon_{YX\overline{c}} = 0.70; \quad C_{YX\overline{c}} = 0.10; \quad \phi_{YX\overline{c}} = 0.53$$

The extent to which economic development (C) does not explain government spending (Y) and voting participation (X) is indicated in Table 5.3.

Data for those two associations are taken from the marginal distributions (usually referred to as the "marginals") of Table 5.2.

Table 5.3. **Associations between economic development, on the one hand, and government spending and voting levels on the other.**

	High development C	Low development $\bar{C}$	
High expenditures Y	11	5	16
Low expenditures $\bar{Y}$	3	7	10
	14	12	26

$$\epsilon_{YC} = 0.37; \quad C_{YC} = 0.092; \quad \phi_{YC} = 0.38$$

	High development C	Low development $\bar{C}$	
High voting X	10	2	12
Low voting $\bar{X}$	4	10	14
	14	12	26

$$\epsilon_{XC} = 0.55; \quad C_{XC} = 0.136; \quad \phi_{XC} = 0.55$$

The relevant ϕ's suggest not only that economic development is positively associated with expenditure levels and voting participation, as socio-economic theories of development imply, but also that both associations are at least as strong as the original one between voting and expenditures.

MEASURES OF CONDITIONAL ASSOCIATION.   A further conclusion from Table 5.2 is that among developed countries, the association between voting and spending has virtually disappeared (notice that the United States is the only developed, low-voting, and low-spending nation of the 26 in the two tables); among underdeveloped nations, however, a strong degree of association between voting and spending seems still to exist. *More precise interpretations of the effects of the control variable C in Table 5.2 depend on calculations of measures of association within groups C and $\bar{C}$.*

An association relationship between two variables, X and Y, in subgroups of a population is usually called a conditional association.

Formulas for conditional associations are exactly analogous to those we have already used for entire populations. In particular, it is possible to define measures of conditional association that correspond to ϵ, δ, C_{YX}, and ϕ in the two-variable case. Relations between these measures, as well as their various computational equivalences, can be demonstrated using the same methods as in Chapter 4. At this point, however, we shall only mention several notational conventions useful for dealing with associations within different control group categories and suggest a few of the relevant derivations.

First, proportions, denoted by P's, and frequencies, symbolized by N's, are interchangeable according to obvious conventions. Using X, Y, and C as subscripts,

$$P_X = \frac{N_X}{N} ; \qquad P_{YX} = \frac{N_{YX}}{N} ; \qquad P_{YXC} = \frac{N_{YXC}}{N} , \qquad \text{etc.} \quad (5.1)$$

Analogous formulas hold when various barred subscripts are systematically introduced, indicating the absence (low value) of a particular attribute. Using this notation, the "criterion of conditional independence between X and Y in C" can be stated in either of the following equivalent fashions:

$$\frac{P_{YXC}}{P_{XC}} = \frac{P_{Y\bar{X}C}}{P_{\bar{X}C}} = \frac{P_{YC}}{P_C} ; \qquad \frac{N_{YXC}}{N_{XC}} = \frac{N_{Y\bar{X}C}}{N_{\bar{X}C}} = \frac{N_{YC}}{N_C} \quad (5.2)$$

In words, we are referring to the situation where the proportion of Y's is the same among X's and $\bar{X}$'s as it is in the marginals for control group C. Variables X and Y are conditionally independent in C if knowing whether X is present or absent does not change the proportions of Y's from its subgroup marginal rate. ϵ_{YXC}, a difference in proportions measure of departure from conditional independence in C, may be defined by subtracting proportions of Y's among X's and $\bar{X}$'s. Subtracting cell frequencies from their expected values in the case of independence gives δ_{YXC}. Taking the difference between actual and expected cell proportions, on the other hand, gives C_{YXC}, which may also be defined in cross-product terms.

Another important notational and conceptual distinction refers to proportions and associations *within* control subgroups rather than among the universe of units being observed. Thus it is possible, and sometimes advantageous, to define proportions in C as fractions of N_C, the subgroup total size, rather than of N, the size of the entire population. Conventionally, primes (' 's) symbolize proportions within control subgroups. The results for Y's are essentially the same as those for X's:

$$P'_{XC} = \frac{N_{XC}}{N_C} ; \qquad P'_{YXC} = \frac{N_{YXC}}{N_C} \qquad (5.3)$$

It will also sometimes be useful to use conditional Q's rather than 1 minus conditional P's:

$$Q'_{XC} = 1 - P'_{XC} = P'_{\bar{X}C} = \frac{N_{\bar{X}C}}{N_C} \qquad (5.4)$$

*Dividing *both* numerators and denominators in these definitions by N (so the values of the entire expressions do not change), we can express primed proportions wholly in terms of unprimed proportions:

$$P'_{XC} = \frac{N_{XC}/N}{N_C/N} = \frac{P_{XC}}{P_C}$$

$$Q'_{XC} = \frac{N_{\bar{X}C}/N}{N_C/N} = \frac{Q_{XC}}{P_C}$$

$$P'_{YXC} = \frac{N_{YXC}/N}{N_C/N} = \frac{P_{YXC}}{P_C} \qquad (5.5)$$

As a general rule, it is clear that *the formulas for within subgroup proportions equal their whole group analogs, divided by the proportional size of the subgroup.*

*What about within subgroup variances and covariances? According to the practice of Chapter 4, variances of X or Y in C (s^2_{XC} or s^2_{YC}) should be equated with within subgroup proportion products:

$$s^2_{XC} = P'_{XC}Q'_{XC} = \frac{P_{XC}Q_{XC}}{P^2_C} ; \qquad s^2_{YC} = P'_{YC}Q'_{YC} = \frac{P_{YC}Q_{YC}}{P^2_C} \qquad (5.6)$$

For covariances, it is again in accord with previous definitions to define a conditional, or within subgroup, covariance (C_{YXC}) as

$$C_{YXC} = P'_{YXC} - (P'_{YXC})_0 = P'_{YXC} - P'_{YC}P'_{XC} \qquad (5.7)$$

Substituting non-primed proportions according to Equation (5.5) gives

$$C_{YXC} = \frac{1}{P_C}\left(P_{YXC} - \frac{P_{YC}P_{XC}}{P_C}\right) \qquad (5.8)$$

*In Equations (5.6) and (5.7) it should be clear that covariances and covariations have been defined in terms of primed subgroup proportions, not universal ones. The non-primed equivalent forms of these definitions in (5.6) and (5.8) have more P_C terms than the primed

Table 5.4. Measures of conditional association between dichotomous attributes X and Y in control group C.

	Definition	Symbol	Formula	Computational alternatives	Equivalent interpretations
1.	Differences in proportions in C	ϵ_{YXC}	$\dfrac{P'_{YXC}}{P'_{XC}} - \dfrac{P'_{Y\overline{X}C}}{P'_{\overline{X}C}}$	$\dfrac{P_{YXC}}{P_{XC}} - \dfrac{P_{Y\overline{X}C}}{P_{\overline{X}C}}$	Slope within subgroup C
2.	Difference from expected cell entry in C	δ_{YXC}	$N_{YXC} - (N_{YXC})_0$	$N_{YXC} - \dfrac{N_{XC}N_{YC}}{N_C}$ or $\dfrac{N_{YXC}N_{\overline{Y}\overline{X}C} - N_{Y\overline{X}C}N_{\overline{Y}XC}}{N_C}$	Covariation within subgroup C
3.	Conditional cross-product	C_{YXC}	$P'_{YXC}P'_{\overline{Y}\overline{X}C} - P'_{Y\overline{X}C}P'_{\overline{Y}XC}$	$\dfrac{\delta_{YXC}}{N_C}$ or $P'_{YXC} - (P'_{YXC})_0$	Covariance within subgroup C
4.	Conditional correlation	ϕ_{YXC}	$\dfrac{C_{YXC}}{s_{YC}s_{XC}}$	$\epsilon_{YXC}\dfrac{P'_X Q'_X}{P'_Y Q'_Y} = \epsilon_{YXCP}\dfrac{P_X Q_X}{_Y Q_Y}$	Standardized covariance, or correlation within subgroup C
5.	Coefficient of conditional determination	ϕ^2_{YXC}	$\dfrac{C^2_{YXC}}{s^2_{YC}s^2_{XC}}$	$(\phi_{YXC})^2$; or $\epsilon_{YXC}\epsilon_{XYC}$	Proportion of conditional variance explained

Notes: Primed proportions refer to proportions of control group totals (N_C). $\overline{C}$ may be substituted for C if done so everywhere in a single equation. It is also useful to remember that $P'_{XC} = P_{XC}/P_C$; $Q'_{XC} = Q_{XC}/Q_C$; $P'_{XC}Q'_{XC} = P'_{XC}Q_{XC} = P_{XC}Q_{XC}/P^2_C$; $s^2_{XC} = Q_{XC}/Q_C$; Similar formulas hold for Y.

ones; therefore, blindly asserting by analogy that conditional variances, for example, have the same *non*-primed formulas as given for simple two-variable associations in Chapter 4 is incorrect. The reader may therefore like to compare the attribute measures of association and their correlational equivalents summarized in Table 5.4 with earlier results in Tables 4.2 and 4.4.

With these coefficients we are finally able precisely to state the effects of controlling for a third variable. One convenient way of visually summarizing the impact of development on the relationship between national voting levels and government expenditures is to calculate and geometrically to display differences in Y-intercepts, slopes, and correlations attributable to the control variable. Relevant formulas for conditional ϵ's (interpreted as slopes) and conditional ϕ's (interpreted as correlation coefficients) are given in Table 5.4; with the exception of the Y-intercepts, values for these coefficients have already been given below the contingency tables, Tables 5.1 and 5.2. Regression lines for underdeveloped countries, developed countries, and the whole "universe" (of 26 countries) are plotted in Figure 5.1.[3]

Figure 5.1 brings out the following theoretically interesting comparisons. They may be interpreted in terms of a linear model because of the way in which the probability of one variable increases with changes in the probability of another.

1. Economic development raises the initial probability of being a high government spender nearly 40 percent among low-voting societies. (The subgroup lines are farthest apart at their Y-intercepts.)

2. Compared to the universal figure, economic underdevelopment nearly doubles the extent to which voting increases are associated with spending level increases.

3. Underdevelopment *increases* the worldwide correlation between voting and spending by 0.12 to 0.53 while development *decreases* the universal figure to about one-eighth of its previous value. (ϕ^2 differences are even greater.)

B.   The Analysis of Covariance: A General Formulation

In interpreting the results in Tables 5.1 and 5.2, we have asked two basic questions: how are associations within categories of a control

---

[3] These regressions for dummy variable interpretations of dichotomous attributes were plotted in the same manner as Figure 4.3. Y-intercepts equal $\overline{Y} - b\overline{X}$, or, in the current interpretation, $P_Y - \epsilon_{YX} \cdot P_X$. Relevant proportions may be found in the margins of Tables 5.1 and 5.2.

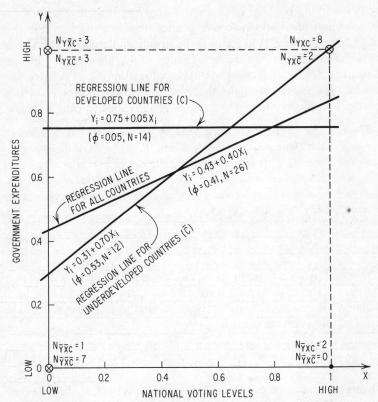

FIGURE 5.1 The conditioning effect of economic development on the relation between national voting levels and government expenditures. Regressions for different values of the control variable are superimposed on the worldwide relationship.

Source: see note 3.

variable related to each other, and to the universal relationship being studied? And what relation does the control variable have to the other variables involved?

THE COVARIANCE THEOREM FOR DICHOTOMOUS ATTRIBUTES. Surprisingly enough, there is a single equation, a simple mathematical tautology, that, when properly interpreted, relates the answers to these two separate questions. In general terms, the basic result states that a universal, overall covariance (or correlation) is a weighted average of covariances *within* control subgroups of the universe and, additionally, of a term relating *between* subgroup differences of the independent and dependent variables. We shall soon illustrate the theorem's utility in clarifying political inferences, in studying the interrelationships between individual and collective political characteristics, and in distinguishing between time series comparisons and those taken at one cross-section in time. In the next chapter it will also be used in constructing a definition of two-variable causal relationships. After understanding the statement of the theorem, the cursory reader is advised to skip immediately to the discussion of fallacious inferences below.

Theorem 5.1   (The covariance theorem for dichotomous attributes). For any two dichotomous attributes X and Y, and a third dichotomized "control" variable C, it is possible to equate the universal cross-product C_{YX} with a weighted average of covariances within control subgroups, and, additionally, a term involving a product of the covariances between Y and C, and C and X.[4] *Specifically,*

$$C_{YX} = P_C C_{YXC} + P_{\overline{C}} C_{YX\overline{C}} + \frac{C_{YC} \cdot C_{CX}}{P_C \cdot P_{\overline{C}}} \qquad (5.9)$$

*Tactics. An algebraic proof of this theorem is short and quite easy to follow. The basic approach will be to add the compact non-primed formulas for conditional cross-products found in Equation (5.8). The result should eventually equal

$$C_{YX} - \frac{C_{YC} \cdot C_{CX}}{P_C P_{\overline{C}}}, \qquad (5.10)$$

the terms equal to the conditional cross-products in (5.9). Putting both terms in (5.10) over the same denominator, and substituting $P_{YC} - (P_{YC})_0$ type definitions for $C_{YX'}$, C_{YC}, and $C_{CX'}$, it is clear that our target should look like

$$\frac{P_C P_{\overline{C}}(P_{YX} - P_Y P_X) - (P_{YC} - P_Y P_C)(P_{CX} - P_C P_X)}{P_C P_{\overline{C}}} \qquad (5.11)$$

---

[4] Yule was the first to establish this result for dichotomous attributes; Paul Lazarsfeld deserves credit for bringing it to the focus of attention of American social scientists. See especially his "Evidence and Inference in Social Research," *Daedalus*, **87**, 4 (Fall 1958).

At this point it might also be worthwhile to give an equivalent result for dummy variable correlations (i.e., ϕ's). This and similar results for δ's and ϵ's are immediately obtainable from the theorem by making the proper substitutions. Using the definitions and computational equivalents given in Table 5.4, it follows that

$$\phi_{YX} = \frac{\phi_{YXC}}{P_C} \cdot \sqrt{\frac{P_{XC} Q_{XC} P_{YC} Q_{YC}}{P_X Q_X P_Y Q_Y}} + \frac{\phi_{XY\overline{C}}}{P_{\overline{C}}} \cdot \sqrt{\frac{P_{X\overline{C}} Q_{X\overline{C}} P_{Y\overline{C}} Q_{Y\overline{C}}}{P_X Q_X P_Y Q_Y}} + \phi_{YC} \phi_{CX}$$

$$(5.9a)$$

Notice how this expression contains no two-letter negative (barred) subscripts.

Proof: Going back to the cross-products as defined in Equation (5.8), we can construct a weighted average of C_{YXC} and $C_{YX\overline{C}}$ as follows:

$$P_C C_{YXC} = P_{YXC} - \frac{P_{YC} \cdot P_{XC}}{P_C}$$

$$P_{\overline{C}} C_{YX\overline{C}} = P_{YX\overline{C}} - \frac{P_{Y\overline{C}} \cdot P_{X\overline{C}}}{P_{\overline{C}}} \qquad (5.12)$$

Adding these expressions, simplifying the first term on the right, and using a common denominator $P_C P_{\overline{C}}$, we have

$$P_C C_{YXC} + P_{\overline{C}} C_{YXC} = \frac{P_C P_{\overline{C}} P_{XY} - P_{\overline{C}} P_{XC} P_{YC} - P_C P_{X\overline{C}} P_{Y\overline{C}}}{P_C P_{\overline{C}}}$$

$$(5.13)$$

In terms of the goal suggested in (5.11), it would be desirable to substitute $P_X - P_{XC}$ for $P_{X\overline{C}}$ and $P_Y - P_{YC}$ for $P_{Y\overline{C}}$ to eliminate the negative subscripts in the last term of Equation (5.13). Multiplying out the right side of (5.13) with these substitutions gives

$$\frac{P_C P_{\overline{C}} P_{XY} - \overbrace{P_{\overline{C}} P_{XC} P_{YC}} - P_C P_X P_Y \cdot (P_C + P_{\overline{C}}) + P_C P_Y P_{YC} + P_C P_X P_{YC} - \overbrace{P_C P_{XC} P_{YC}}}{P_C P_{\overline{C}}}$$

$$(5.14)$$

The bracketed terms can immediately be added to produce one of the desired terms (see Equation 5.11); checked terms are already appropriate. Now we need only a $P_C P_{\overline{C}} P_X P_Y$ to complete the C_{YX} and a $P_X P_Y P_C^2$ term to make the $C_{YC} \cdot C_{CX}$ product required in (5.11). Inserting $(P_C + P_{\overline{C}})$, which equals one, in front of $P_C P_X P_Y$ gives the desired result without changing the value of (5.15):

$$= P_{XY} - P_X P_Y + \frac{(P_{XC} - P_X P_C)(P_{YC} - P_Y P_C)}{P_C P_{\overline{C}}} \qquad (5.15)$$

$$= C_{XY} - \frac{C_{XC} \cdot C_{YC}}{P_C P_{\overline{C}}} \qquad Q.E.D.$$

ALTERNATIVE VERSIONS OF THE COVARIANCE THEOREM. Before illustrating some of its uses, it will be helpful to state without formal proofs several more general versions of the covariance theorem. If X and Y are interval variables, Theorem 5.2 gives a simple but extremely powerful result:

Theorem 5.2 (The covariance theorem for interval variables). If X and Y are measured on at least an interval scale, and covariances are calculated both within and between two or more categories of a control variable, then the total covariance equals the sum of the within and between covariances. Symbolically,

$$C_{XY} \quad = \quad WC_{XY} \quad + \quad BC_{XY} \qquad (5.16)^5$$

Total covariance = within covariance + between covariance

The "between subgroups" term (BC_{XY}) is the covariance of subgroup means on X and Y about their universal means, each subgroup mean being counted as many times as there are units of data in the subgroup; the "within subgroup covariance" (WC_{XY}) is a weighted average of covariances for each control category, just like in the special dichotomous case ($C, \overline{C}$) of Theorem 5.1 above.

*Coming back to the case of three dichotomous "dummy variables" (e.g., Theorem 5.1), Theorem 5.2 says that the within subgroup covariance is a sum of two conditional terms:

$$WC_{XY} = \sum_{\substack{i=C \\ \text{and } \overline{C}}} P_i C_{YXi} \qquad (5.17)$$

exactly as in Theorem 5.1, and that

$$BC_{XY} = \frac{1}{N} \sum_{\substack{i=C \\ \text{and } \overline{C}}} N_i(P'_{Xi} - P_X)(P'_{Yi} - P_Y) \qquad (5.18)$$

Comparing the two theorems shows that the between subgroup covariance BC_{XY} must equal the product of covariances term[6]:

$$BC_{XY} = \frac{C_{XC}C_{CY}}{P_C P_{\overline{C}}} \qquad (5.19)$$

---

[5] For definitions of these covariances using double summation signs, as well as a proof of (5.16), the reader is referred to H. M. Blalock, Jr., *Social Statistics*, (New York: McGraw-Hill, 1960), Chapter 20, or H. M. Walker and J. Lev, *Statistical Inference* (New York: Holt, Rinehart and Winston, 1953), Chapter 15. The basic idea is simply to sum a tautology: If X_{ij} is the value of X for individual i in group j, $\overline{X}_j$ is the mean of group j and $\overline{X}$ the universal mean, etc., the tautology is

$$(X_{ij} - \overline{X})(Y_{ij} - \overline{Y}) = [(X_{ij} - \overline{X}_j) + (\overline{X}_j - \overline{X})][(Y_{ij} - \overline{Y}_j) + (\overline{Y}_j - \overline{Y})]$$

[6] The curious reader may like to try establishing the dichotomous case result in (5.19) to his or her own satisfaction. A successful approach is first to substitute non-primed equivalents into (5.18), then to get rid of negative (barred) double subscripts, and finally to use the $1 = P_C + P_{\overline{C}}$ trick to generate the right-hand side of (5.19). The proof is similar to the one given above for Theorem 5.1.

A main reason for this result (hinted at in the above discussion of Table 5.3) is that both sides of Equation (5.19) are calculated from subgroup marginal proportions.[7]

SOME RECURRING FALLACIES IN POLITICAL INFERENCE. Both politicians and political analysts are tempted to make wishful but inaccurate inferences from incomplete or unrepresentative information. The covariance theorem proved above indicates several ways of falling (or plunging) into this trap, measures the extent to which these fallacies have occurred, and suggests some less obvious research directions for avoiding them.

The class of inferential fallacies indicated by the covariance theorem concerns inferences from one level of generality to another. As schematized in Figure 5.2, the covariance theorem relates three different "levels of analysis":

(1) universal or total covariances (C_{YX});

(2) within subgroup covariances (such as C_{YXr} or $C_{YX\bar{r}}$);

(3) between subgroup covariances (BC_{YXR} or EC_{YXR}).

Essentially the same distinctions are made by all the versions of the covariance theorem discussed above, including those using cross-products and correlations.

As symbolized in Figure 5.2, the same abstract algebraic formula can be subjected to quite different substantive interpretations. In the list of recurring fallacies in political rhetoric given below, the control variable (R) will sometimes be substantively interpreted as: a *regional* classification (e.g., r = North, $\bar{r}$ = South in the United States), as a *temporal* ordering (e.g., r = one year, $\bar{r}$ = the next), or a *socio-political* distinction (like r = Republican, $\bar{r}$ = Democrat). The abstractness of the mathematics adds considerably to its usefulness for formulating general rules for all interpretations as to when inferences from one level of generality to another are valid or invalid. For now, we shall assume that the different covariances indicated in Figure 5.2 are *unequal* and list some rather obvious examples when various political arguments have incorrectly suggested inferences from one kind of covariance to another.[8]

[7] A well-known controversy in sociology concerning ecological correlations (to be discussed below) centers on another version of the covariance theorem for interval scales. An excellent summary of the literature, including contributions by W. S. Robinson and Leo Goodman, may be found in O. D. Duncan, R. P. Cuzzort and B. Duncan, *Statistical Geography* (New York: The Free Press of Glencoe, 1961).

[8] Another way of generating fallacies would be to assume that individual regional and between group correlations are equal and think of examples where people have erroneously said they were different. To the extent that stereotypes are not valid generalizations, for example, they usually err in this direction.

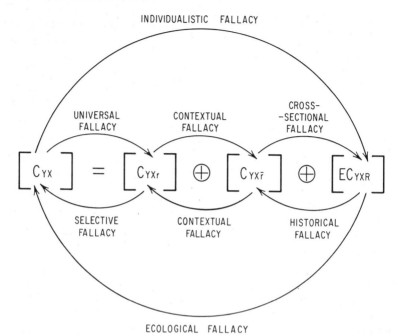

FIGURE 5.2   A covariance scheme for labelling certain recurring fallacies in political inference. (If all covariances are in fact unequal, each label refers to an incorrect inference.)

Note: Schematized equation is The Covariance Theorem as applied to two "regions" of data (r and $\bar{r}$, together R). In left to right order, the covariances are for (1) the universe of data, (2) region r, (3) region $\bar{r}$, and (4) ecological, i.e., regional averages.

1. *The Ecological Fallacy.*   W. S. Robinson has called attention to some important problems in interpreting census data or other aggregative information published only for groups.   First, he distinguished individual (i.e., universal) correlations from ecological (i.e., between group) correlations.   Individual correlations describe objects which are indivisible.   Ecological correlations (which themselves often have intrinsic interest) correlate percentage information about groups of individuals, such as voting precincts, states, or regions.   Robinson warns against inferring without investigation that relationships among collectivities are the same as those for individuals.   Only under very specific circumstances (to be discussed below) are such inferences from ecological data valid; otherwise the observer has committed the *ecological fallacy.*

Robinson gives two examples of the ecological fallacy, motives for which are not difficult to imagine.   The first concerns the relationship between Negro race and literacy in the United States.   The ϕ correlation for a 2 × 2 table of the entire population over 10 years old *taken individually* is about 0.20. Grouping the data into 48 states and correlating their marginal percentages of Negro and illiterate inhabitants produces a product-moment ecological correlation of 0.77! Grouping states into nine regions as defined by the Census Bureau gives a fantastically high ecological correlation of 0.95! Inferring a relationship of this magnitude to hold for individual Negroes may be politically expedient, even when inappropriate, as the small ϕ correlation for individuals (0.20) shows.

In a second example, Robinson found that a regional ecological correlation between foreign birth and illiteracy (a perennial topic for election year xenophobia) is highly negative: −0.62. When computed individually, however, the correlation for a 2 × 2 table (illiteracy versus foreign birth) actually comes out positive: 0.12. Although this individual correlation is very small (it explains less than 2 percent of the variance), the fact that it is positive while the ecological correlation is negative dramatically illustrates the problems of ecological inference. A third variable, such as urbanization, probably accounts for a good deal of the literacy as well as higher percentages of foreign born.

2. *The Individualistic Fallacy.* The individualistic fallacy is just the opposite of the ecological fallacy. For ideological reasons, liberal social scientists are also likely to try to generalize from individual behavior to aggregative relationships. To assume that competition among individuals will universally produce industrious citizens does not mean, *necessarily*, that the nation with the most competitors will be the most industrious. Laissez faire arguments need to be independently validated at all levels of cooperation and competition.

3. *The Universal Fallacy.* Political science generalists in theory or policy-making are especially susceptible to another kind of fallacious inference. Professionally they must try to infer statements with regional validity from imperfectly valid universal generalizations. To cite an example of the universal fallacy where the evidence has already been presented, the universal relationship between national voting participation and government spending does not appear to hold for economically developed countries (see Table 5.2).[9]

[9] More examples of this kind of analysis have been presented in Alker, "Regionalism versus Universalism in Comparing Nations," in Russett and Alker, Deutch, Lasswell, *op. cit.* Professor Erwin Scheuch has called attention to a similar problem in his "Cross-National Comparisons Using Aggregate Data: Some Substantive and Methodological Problems," in R. Merritt and S. Rokkan, *Comparing Nations* (New Haven: Yale University Press, 1965), Chapter 10, although his term "individualistic fallacy" seems also to refer to the kind of inference discussed above under that label.

4. *The Selective Fallacy.* As Figure 5.2 indicates, the selective fallacy is logically opposite to the universal one. Selecting evidence that fits one's interpretation is applauded in politics but frowned upon by academics. Suppose Senator Foghorn thinks Democratic Senators do "more" for their constituencies because he can most eloquently "recall" several Democratic colleagues (possibly including himself) who have recently been especially attentive to the needs of their home districts. Let us call those political districts where Foghorn's generalizations *are* valid region *r*. Having listened to the Senator's "recollections," most Republicans would dispute the validity of the Senator's contention, at least in region $\bar{r}$, and certainly for the nation as a whole.

5. *The Contextual Fallacy.* It is possible to confuse valid interpretations in one region or time period or context with those in another. The right kind of American response toward Cuba and toward Vietnam provoke these kinds of controversies. Administration critics might argue that *if* it were "right" for the United States to bomb North Vietnam in 1965, it would have been "right" to bomb then in the Bay of Pigs invasion of 1962. Defenders of both policies would argue that the situations were different: they occurred in different *regions* (in relation to the kinds of force that could easily be brought to bear), at different *times* (since the Cuban missile crisis the Communists are not as likely to misperceive a limited use of force), and in disparate *contexts* (the directness of the provocation toward the United States). Since the number of recent international conflict situations is limited, and since there will always be difficult problems of not selecting misleading analogies, foreign policy controversies almost always contain regional, temporal, or contextual fallacies.

6. *The Historical Fallacy.* Arguments starting with "history shows that" may or may not be true. Inferences from "longitudinal" historical trends to cross-sectional comparisons for the present day certainly require further exploration. For example, although it is obvious that Communist countries have grown militarily stronger since 1917, it does not follow necessarily that *now* they are stronger than non-Communist countries.

7. *The Cross-sectional Fallacy.* To take the logically opposite kind of inference (one political scientists are more likely to make), neither can it be said that cross-sectional comparisons at one point in time *necessarily* indicate historically how certain variables have been related. More urbanized and developed countries currently have less domestic group violence (a correlation to be discussed below). Compared with the nineteenth century, however, it does not logically follow that urbanization has brought domestic peace. As shown in Theorem

5.1, time changes must be correlated with increasing urbanization and decreasing domestic violence for such an inference to be valid.[10]

INFERENCES FROM ONE COVARIANCE TO ANOTHER. The covariance theorem indicates in a rather obvious way how inferences about one covariance from another may go wrong; much more importantly, it allows us to *calculate* and *explain* differences among two covariances in terms of a third covariance; and most importantly, it suggests mathematical ways of formulating and testing appropriate explanatory models in these very situations where such inferential fallacies as those outlined above are likely to occur. These methods go considerably beyond the measures of conditional association already introduced.

To illustrate these points, let us reconsider the covariance theorem for dichotomous attributes, as it applies to the covariance between government spending (Y) and voting levels (X) previously discussed. Using r to represent economically developed "regions," $\bar{r}$ to denote underdeveloped ones, and R to symbolize the dichotomous attribute development, Theorems 5.1 and 5.2 imply that

$$
\begin{array}{lll}
\text{Total Covariance} = & \text{Within regions} & + \text{Between regions} \\
& \text{covariance} & \text{covariance} \\
C_{YX} & = 0.54 C_{YXr} + 0.46 C_{YX\bar{r}} + & 4.1 C_{YR} \cdot C_{RX} \\
(0.10) & 0.54(0.01) \quad 0.46(0.10) & 4.1(0.09)(0.14) \\
0.10 & = \qquad 0.05 & + \qquad 0.05
\end{array}
$$

$$(5.20)$$

The proportions P_C and $P_{\bar{C}}$ have been replaced by their respective values, 0.54 and 0.46 (see Tables 5.1 to 5.3). Equation (5.20) makes very clear how inference from one level of analysis to another might

[10] Karl Deutsch and his colleagues have made several explicit comparisons of longitudinal (over time) and cross-sectional (at one time) political relationships. Studying the general hypothesis of increasing nationalism in world politics, they found that, cross-sectionally, larger and more developed countries have less foreign trade contacts (as a percentage of Gross National Products), and, longitudinally, that most countries in the North Atlantic area have also decreased foreign trade/GNP ratios since the first two decades of this century. See Karl W. Deutsch and Alexander Eckstein, "National Industrialization and the Declining Share of the International Economic Sector, 1890–1959, *World Politics*, **13**, 2 (January 1961), pp. 267–299, and K. W. Deutsch, C. I. Bliss, A. Eckstein, "Population, Sovereignty, and the Share of Foreign Trade," *Economic Development and Cultural Change*, **10**, 4 (July 1962), pp. 353–1366.

Duncan, Cuzzort, and Duncan, *op. cit.*, have imaginatively explored the same conceptual problem, using the ecological correlation version of the covariance theorem. Their writing led to the "cross-sectional" and "historical" (i.e., longitudinal) labels in Figure 5.2. One of their most interesting suggestions is that a cross-section at one point in time can be considered exactly analogous to one set of interviews in a panel survey. Few of the theories and methodologies of this kind of survey analysis have been applied to cross-national comparisons.

be confusing. First, total covariances and between region covariances are not the same because within region covariances have to be taken into account. That is why the ecological correlation will not account for the individual one. In fact, as has already been illustrated the ecological (between group) correlation will be positive even though the individual correlation is negative whenever the within group covariance is negative and larger in magnitude than the between group one!

Focusing on the within group correlations, we can say specifically what the total effect of controlling for development was, and why it occurred. The covariance theorem tells us to form a weighted average of within group covariances [indicated below Equation (5.20)], and to identify the result as the total within region covariance. This sum is about 0.05, indicating that *half* the total covariance of 0.10 reported in Table 5.1 remains after levels of development have been controlled for. The equation suggests, moreover, where the rest of the covariance has gone! The previously suspicious effects of the intercorrelations of R with X and Y are confirmed to the precise extent that a between region covariance also accounts for half of the original covariance and that this effect of correlations among regional marginals takes the form of a product of two covariances, C_{YR} and C_{RX} (given in Table 5.3), multiplied by the inverse of the product of r and $\bar{r}$ proportions. Ecological correlations will disappear, however, when either or both of these covariances is zero.

Unless these results are known, the casual observer of Tables 5.1 and 5.3 is likely to make every one of the fallacies described in Figure 5.2! Without the covariance theorem, even knowing the partial covariances given for Table 5.2 does not prevent any of four fallacious inferences involving ecological correlations.[11]

C. Multivariate Theories about Politics

The covariance theorem suggests many ways of formulating multivariate (many-variabled) theories of political analysis. In the discussion of conditional regressions explaining government spending, two main ways were mentioned in which a control variable could combine with

[11] Although we shall not fully develop the point here, it should be noted that it is possible to give a theoretical basis for making inferences from ecological to individual correlations. Assuming that slopes and intercepts for individual relationships are the same in each region of data, Leo Goodman has proposed using regression techniques for estimating individual parameters from aggregate data. He tests for the validity of his assumption by looking at how residuals from a regression of Y on X cluster around the regression live. For more details the interested reader is referred to the sources cited in footnote 7 above.

another explanatory variable X. First, we could think of a control variable *adding* to the overall level of the dependent variable Y; secondly, it might *change the form* of the relationship between X and Y. In either case individual conditional correlations might be strengthened or weakened; taking into account the effects of a second variable could not help, however, but improve the total explanatory power of a three-variable model compared to a two-variable model.

ADDITIVE THEORIES OF VIOLENCE. Let us test the following set of hypotheses relating land inequality to the number of deaths per million population resulting from domestic group violence. On the basis of earlier investigations[12] we assume

(1) that land inequality causes violence;

(2) that a high level of agricultural employment (indicating fewer social opportunities, fewer increases in wealth, power, and other desired values) also causes violence;

(3) that these two causes are independent of each other and combine additively in raising violence levels;

(4) that violence not explained by these variables is a random phenomenon (an oversimplification).

It is possible to express this simple theory in the following symbolic fashion (where Y = Violence, X_1 = Inequality, X_2 = Agricultural Labor Force, a is a constant, and u is a randomly changing variable):

$$Y = a + b_{Y1 \cdot 2}X_1 + b_{Y2 \cdot 1}X_2 + u \qquad (5.21)$$

The reader should recognize this kind of "multiple regression" equation as a generalization of the linear regression equation to the multivariate case. Now, instead of one explanatory variable, there are two, each with a partial slope (b) indicating the change in Y resulting from a change in a particular X, controlling for the effect of the other explanatory variable.[13]

---

[12] Some of the relevant literature is summarized in B. M. Russett, "Inequality and Instability, The Relation of Land Tenure to Politics," *World Politics*, **16**, 3 (April 1964), pp. 442–454. Russett found agricultural labor force and land inequality to be the most important variables in a five-variable linear additive regression equation explaining half the variance in domestic group violence. His results were for four fewer political units.

[13] Partial slopes for interval variables in one sense "average" the effects of differences in within region slopes. They are defined by the following equation:

$$b_{YX \cdot C} = \frac{b_{YX} - b_{YC}b_{CX}}{1 - b_{XC}b_{CX}} \qquad (5.22)$$

Solving for b_{YX} suggests how this formula could be derived from Theorems 5.2 and the relevant definitions. In passing, it might also be noted that *curvilinear* regressions can be calculated by the same method as Equations (5.21) and (5.22). X_2 need only be calculated as $X_1{}^2$!

Testing such a model leads to the following encouraging results:

$$r_{YX_1}^2 \text{ (land)} = 0.22$$
$$r_{YX_2}^2 \text{ (labor)} = 0.45$$
$$R_{Y.12}^2 \text{ (both)} = 0.56 \qquad (5.23)$$

First, notice how strongly both explanatory variables influence Y. Each contributes more than 10 percent of the variance explained by the multiple regression model. The fairly high multiple correlation coefficient $R_{Y.12}$ indicates the total variance explained when both independent variables are joined in an additive fashion.[14]

MULTIPLICATIVE THEORIES OF VIOLENCE. It is plausible to think of variables like agricultural ruralism adding to level of violence while also multiplicatively affecting the slope of another explanatory relationship such as between land inequality and violence. Verbally, multiplicating relations appear in such phrases as "the effect of X is *intensified by or inhibited by Y*." Unlike the additive model previously discussed, multiplicative models do not ignore (or take "averages" of) within subgroup slopes that may be very different. Multiplicative relationships can be studied for either attributes (as in Figure 5.1) or for interval and ratio scales (as in Figure 5.3).

Taking a different control variable from the one discussed above, let us test for the additive and multiplicative effects of European culture (an overall label serving to distinguish between European and non-European countries) on domestic group violence. Because of the high level of economic development in most European countries and their wider range of cultural opportunities, etc., we would hypothesize that, additively, European nations have lower levels of violence than non-European countries. Multiplicatively, it also seems reasonable to expect European culture to have a depressing effect on proportionate increases in violence resulting from a unit increase in land inequality. In Figure 5.3 separate linear regressions for European (including the United States and white members of the Commonwealth) and non-European countries reveals some remarkable disparities. A rather strong and positive universal relationship between land inequality and domestic group violence is not typical of either European or non-

---

[14] The actual regression calculations (leading to a b coefficient for land of 42.0 and one for labor of 0.50) were performed for logged violence data because some of the smaller differences between relatively peaceful countries would otherwise be submerged by the much larger violence figures for South Vietnam and Cuba (in the thousands per year).

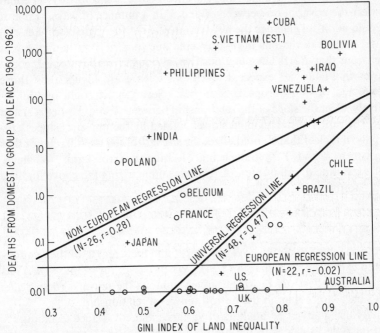

FIGURE 5.3 Regional varieties of a universal relationship. Linear regressions between land inequality and logarithms of domestic group violence, universally and among European and non-European countries.
Notes: (1) European data are indicated by circles 0.
(2) Data for S. Vietnam and Libya are estimated.
(3) No violence levels are assumed lower than 0.01.
Source: See note 3.

European countries when considered independently of each other. Both European and non-European regressions have Y-intercepts *above* that of the universal relationship. Although neither regression slopes as steeply upward as does the universal relationship, European culture does have the hypothesized depressant effect on the relationship between land inequality and domestic group violence—so much so that this relationship for Europeans is very weak, at a low-level of violence and negative in inclination!

It is possible to construct multiplicative formalizations of this kind of relationship in the following manner. First assume that the universal regression can be written

$$Y = a + b \cdot X + u \qquad (5.24)$$

Clearly, another variable (like European culture and history, e) could affect the covariation between X and Y in a number of ways. First, it could additively change the *level* or *intercept* of the regression. Let $d(e)$ and $d(\bar{e})$ be deviations in Y-intercepts due to e. From the figure it is obvious that $d(e)$ is large and positive, although for all European countries in Figure 5.3 expected levels of violence are higher than those expected of non-European countries. Secondly, it could multiplicatively affect the *slope* of the relationship between X and Y. Let $s(e)$ and $s(\bar{e})$ be ratios of the regional slopes divided by the universal slopes. Finally, it is clear that e could affect the *strength* of the overall relationship between X and Y by influencing the random error term. Whatever the resulting u, call it $u'(e)$. A formula summarizing the above findings in additive and multiplicative terms is

$$\left. \begin{aligned} Y(X, i) &= a + d(i) + s(i) \cdot b \cdot X + u'(i) \\ i &= e \quad \text{or} \quad \bar{e} \end{aligned} \right\} \tag{5.25}$$

As i changes, so do the level, the slope, and the strength of the relationship expressed in Equation (5.24). When $i = e$, for example, $d(i)$ has a positive effect on Y, $s(i)$ negatively inhibits the universal b and $u'(i)$ is much larger than in the overall universal relationship.

By using advanced analysis of variance and covariance techniques it is possible to calculate the amount of variance in Y that can be explained by introducing each of the assumptions we have made about the effect of e on the covariance of X and Y.[15] The following conclusions emerge from such an analysis. First, 22 percent of the variance in Y can be explained by a universal regression line; replacing this line by two regional regressions with parallel inclinations (equal slopes) adds an amazingly large 38 percent to the variance explained. Introducing into our explanatory model a multiplicative effect which causes the slope on the regression model in (5.25) to vary as a function of e explains only about 1 percent of the cross-national variance in violence levels.

After taking both intercept and slope effects into account, the typical European nation has a much lower level of violence than the average non-European one. In other words, the effect of "European history, culture and geography," as we have lumped them together, is additively to increase (Y-intercept) while multiplicatively reducing the slope of the universal linear regression. In terms of additional variance ex-

[15] An excellent introduction to the analysis of variance and covariance for interval variables may be found in H. M. Blalock, *Social Statistics* (New York: McGraw-Hill, 1960), Chapters 16 and 20.

plained, the additive change is much more important.[16]   Taken together in this fashion, the "regional" variable e and the land inequality index X_1 explain about 62 percent of the total variance in national levels of domestic violence.   Regional contexts, with additive and multiplicative effects, shape and twist what would otherwise be universal generalizations.   Taking these contextual effects into account helps us both to increase the strength of our explanatory models and to make more complex but still universally valid generalizations.

[16] Other examples of multiplicative explanatory models are frequently used by economists (who add logarithms, i.e., multiply), sociologists, and geographers (see Duncan, Cuzzort, and Duncan, *op. cit.* and James Coleman, *An Introduction to Mathematical Sociology*, (New York: Macmillan, 1964).   In the author's "Regionalism versus Universalism," *op. cit.*, there are political science examples of multiplicative terms explaining more variance than additive terms.   In the above example, logged violence data has been used, suggesting that violence is *exponentially* related to European culture and agricultural inequality.   In this regard, note the logarithmic scale in Figure 5.3.

CHAPTER 6

Correlation and Causation

> *... the term "cause," carefully scrubbed free of any undesirable philosophic adhesions, can perform a useful function. ...*
>
> HERBERT SIMON

USING PREVIOUSLY DEVELOPED TOOLS for correlation and covariance analysis, this chapter focuses on the constructive task of distinguishing causally significant relationships from illusory associations. Our concern is no longer with testing inferences from different levels of analysis; however, the basic mathematical formulas are the same. The analysis serves as a final example of how content-free mathematical formulations can be applied to a whole variety of recurring problems in political analysis with significant results.

After reviewing Paul Lazarsfeld's classification of social science explanations, we compare his definition of a causal association with that of Herbert Simon. Finally, Simon's ways of algebraically deriving predictions from causal models are illustrated and then used to test some concrete and controversial causal hypotheses.[1]

A. Evidence and Inference

FOUR KINDS OF EXPLANATION. Lazarsfeld's work on explanations of social behavior closely parallels the approach of the previous chapter. He states that, "Explanation consists of the formal aspect of elaboration and some substantive ordering of variables." Three components of this definition need further exposition: his meanings of "elaboration," of its "formal aspect," and of "some substantive ordering of variables."

---

[1] Lazarsfeld's relevant work includes "Evidence and Inference in Social Research," *Daedalus* **87**, 4 (Fall 1958), and "The Algebra of Dichotomous Systems," in H. Solomon (ed.). *Item Analysis and Prediction* (Stanford: Stanford University Press, 1959). Simon's early articles are reprinted in his *Models of Man, Social and Rational* (New York: Wiley, 1957). For our purposes the most important of these is "Spurious Correlation: a Causal Interpretation," Chapter 2. An exciting, readable exposition and development of Simon's approach is Hubert M. Blalock, Jr., *Causal Inference in Nonexperimental Research* (Chapel Hill: University of North Carolina Press, 1964).

Each helps identify the inferences one can make from concrete evidence of a correlation between variables X and Y.

By *elaboration* he means decomposing a universe of data into different subgroups and studying the correlations between X and Y in each subgroup. In the previous chapter the more general term "cross-tabulation" was used to describe exactly this operation in the dichotomous attribute case. Lazarsfeld calls within group cross-products "partial cross-products" and the between group covariance a "marginal term." Categories of a control variable C define the subgroups of the elaboration process.

His possible *substantive orderings* include those mentioned previously as well as some others:

We have ... focused on ordering by time sequence .... We can [also] distinguish orders of complexity such as variables characterizing persons, collectives, and sets of collectives. Other ordering principles could be introduced, e.g., degree of generality, exemplified by the instance of a specified opinion, a broader attitude, and a basic value system.[2]

The substantive ordering, most typically historical time sequence, relates X, Y and the control variable C.

By the *formal aspect* of an elaboration, he means two extreme possible configurations of the Covariance Theorem: those cases when the marginal covariance disappears or when the total partial covariance disappears. All possible three-variable relationships fall between these extremes.

Putting together these formal aspects of a temporal ordering of an elaborated relationship, Lazarsfeld distinguishes four possible "ideal types" of explanation, out of which all others can be built. As summarized in Table 6.1, all explanations of Y depend on the effects of control variables and of the substantive ordering of X and C.[3]

Each of these possibilities has an appealing social science interpretation. When the partials disappear after C is introduced, the relationship between X and Y depends wholly on marginal associations. If the control variable "washing out" the partials comes *before* X, the rela-

[2] Lazarsfeld, The Algebra of Dichotomous Systems, *op. cit.*, p. 147.

[3] Two simplifications in the above approach should be mentioned. For purposes of exposition Lazarsfeld does not study temporal coincidences (e.g., C and X occur together). Secondly, his later work has focused on an additional parameter, roughly the difference between slopes in two different partial tables. This difference is of interest even in the case when the sum of partial covariances is zero. Otherwise, strong but oppositely inclined partial associations adding to zero would be ignored. Multiplicative methods for describing this possibility have already been given in Chapter 5.

Table 6.1. Four "ideal" ways of interpreting the covariance between
X and Y, controlling for variable C.

	C comes before X and Y	C comes between X and Y
Partial terms sum to zero	X is *spuriously related* to Y	C *intervenes* between X and Y
Marginal term disappears	C is a *prior condition* of the impact of X on Y	The impact of X is *contingent* on C

tionship between X and Y is *spurious*, due only to a prior variable
associated with both. Lazarsfeld suggests how the size of a fire (C)
shows the relationship between the number of fire engines (X) and the
fire damage (Y) to be spurious. A more controversial interpretation
is that Negro civil rights activity (X) does not cause racial riots (Y),
as some would maintain, but that a prior variable, such as Negro
discontent or social injustice (C), makes this relationship between X
and Y a spurious one.

The case where partials disappear and C intervenes between X and
Y can be illustrated in many political ways. The President's actions
(X) in support of the Civil Rights Law may explain subsequent public
compliance (Y) even though the partial terms disappear when the
efforts of local officials (C) are controlled for. How well he persuades
state and local officials to comply and how effective their actions are
may be the *intervening* relationships making up a positive marginal
term.

Cases where the marginals disappear, or nearly disappear, suggest
that the researcher focus on differences in the conditional cross-
products and on average partial slopes and ϕ's, as done in Chapter 5.
When a C comes *before* X and Y and is not related to X or Y or both,
it "conditions" the impact of X on Y. For example, war may be a
prior condition for the Republicans' getting higher voting support. If,
on the other hand, C comes *between* X and Y, a *contingency* exists.
The reelection of harassed Congressmen may or may not be contingent
on Presidential midterm support.

A Definition of the Causal Relation.   Lazarsfeld uses this fourfold classification of explanatory relationships to define the causal relation. In these terms, he states what kind of evidence is necessary for
inferring causation from correlation:

We can suggest a clear-cut definition of the *causal* relation between two attributes. If we have a relationship between X and Y, and if for any antecedent test factor [C], the partial relationships between X and Y do *not* disappear, then the original relationship should be called a causal one.[4]

In other words, *a causal relation is any demonstrable association that is not "spurious."* The basic assumptions and requirements of this approach are two: (1) theoretical assumptions about the (*temporal*) *ordering* of X, Y, and C; and (2) requirements that no antecedent third variable wash out the relationship between X and Y, indicating it to be spurious.

Let us consider a plausible result of a hypothetical experiment using the above definition of a causal relation. What would it mean if the covariance between lack of skill (X) and being unemployed (Y) disappears when we control for inferior education (C)? It seems clear that X is not a cause of Y (otherwise the partials would not have vanished), but what about C? Could C, together with X, be multiple causes of Y? This possibility of a double causation is illustrated in Equation (6.1):

$$\begin{matrix} C \searrow \\ \quad\quad Y \\ X \nearrow \end{matrix} \qquad (6.1)$$

Three more causal relationships become plausible when we rethink the time orderings between C, X and Y. In disallowing a one-arrow causal relation ($X \rightarrow Y$) have we also precluded the possibilities schematized in Equations (6.1) and (6.2), all of which still have X preceding Y?

$$X \rightarrow C \rightarrow Y \qquad (6.2a)$$

$$C \rightarrow X \rightarrow Y \qquad (6.2b)$$

$$\begin{matrix} X & (6.2c) \\ \nearrow & \\ C \longrightarrow Y & \end{matrix}$$

Considerable attention in the sociological literature has been directed toward distinguishing between models (6.2b) and (6.2c), a goal which Lazarsfeld's method does not help us sufficiently to do.[5]

---

[4] Lazarsfeld, "The Algebra of Dichotomous Systems," *op. cit.*, p. 146.

[5] See Patricia Kendall's contributions to Herbert Hyman, *Survey Design and Analysis* (New York: The Free Press of Glencoe, 1955), p. 263, and H. M. Blalock, Jr., "Controlling for Background Factors: Spuriousness Versus Developmental Sequences," *Sociological Inquiry*, **34**, 1 (Winter 1964), pp. 28–40.

B.   Spurious Correlation: A Causal Interpretation

Herbert Simon's approach to causality is a generalization of Lazarsfeld's, in which he introduces a sufficient number of additional theoretical assumptions in order to be able to distinguish cases of "spurious" association (6.2c) from true causal relationships (like the developmental sequence in 6.2b). It assumes interval levels of measurement and easily generalizes to causal relations among more than three variables.

THE RELATION BETWEEN POWER AND CAUSATION. The roots of Simon's approach come directly from problems of political science. In Chapter 2, various definitions of politics were given, all centering on getting values, allocating values, or attaining collective goals. Despite the centrality of decision-making and the related problems of influence and power in modern political analysis,[6] not all students of the subject have been able to agree on how best to proceed.

In approaching the problem of defining *power*, Simon suggests redefining it in terms of the *causal relation* between variables:

... for the assertion, "*A* has power over *B*," we can substitute the assertion, "*A*'s behavior causes *B*'s behavior." If we can define the causal relation, we can define influence, power or authority and *vice versa.*[7]

TWO-VARIABLE CAUSAL RELATIONSHIPS. In this brief review of Simon's method for testing causal hypotheses, we shall first consider two-variable relationships and then three-variable ones. His two-variable description of the causal relationship is quite similar to Lazarsfeld's definition already discussed.

Simon uses three alternative ways of symbolizing causal relationships: arrow diagrams, matrices, and linear equation models. Each symbolism lends itself to different kinds of mathematical treatment according to various rules (matrix analysis or graph theory, for example). After an indication of the "arrow diagram" and matrix approaches, more detailed attention will be given to his algebraic treatment of linear equation models of causal laws.

[6] Robert Dahl, *Modern Political Analysis*, (Englewood Cliffs: Prentice-Hall, 1963), provides an excellent introduction to various ways of measuring power and studying decisions.

[7] Simon, *op. cit.*, pp. 5 and 63–77. Simon also suggests, however, that game theoretical arguments will probably be more helpful in coping with problems of anticipated reactions, unless considerable time lags are involved. Some game theoretic possibilities for the study of power are mentioned briefly in our final chapter.

For two variables of theoretical interest, the statement "X is a cause of Y" can be represented symbolically as

$$X \to Y$$

In this case, the causal relationship (like most definitions of power and influence) is *asymmetrical* (i.e., in one direction only). The same relationship can conveniently be represented in matrix form; asterisks indicate a causal relationship while 0's do not:

		Variable that influences	
		X	Y
Variable being	X	*	0
causally influenced	Y	*	*

The diagonal asterisks show that variables are assumed to influence themselves; the one off-diagonal asterisk indicates that X influences Y, but not *vice versa*.

Simon represents the arrow diagram and the "influence matrix" above by a set of linear equations. *One equation is written for each of the two theoretical variables in the model to indicate what it depends on,* in a manner corresponding to the asterisked matrix entries above. *Independent* variables (like X) that depend only on "themselves" and that are not predicted by the model under consideration are set equal to randomly changing variables, denoted by u's, that are called "error terms."

Dependent variables (like Y) are supposed to change according to causal laws, as described by linear equations. (Non-linear and non-additive cases will not be considered.) The explanatory variables in an equation correspond to off-diagonal asterisked matrix entries. It is also assumed that random phenomena will affect a linear relationship, making exact predictions (e.g., of Y from X) impossible. A random (unpredicted) influence is indicated in a linear equation by another u, which is also called the "error term" or the "residual term." Using such random terms means that deterministic models are not possible, that predictions can only be probabilistic, and that non-random theoretical systems of equations only partly predict behavior.

In a complete set of such equations the omnipotent observer should be able empirically to change the values of the error terms and the independent variables and produce exactly the predicted result. In this sense *the linear equations are assumed to have operating or manipulative significance and may be called "linear (causal) mechanisms."* Seeding rainclouds with dry ice would be a practical example of a causal mechanism.

The same set of equations is supposed to be true for all the individuals in a universe. Using N to denote the number of individuals (either clouds or people or nations) and i to indicate the particular individual being referred to ($i = 1, \ldots, N$), the one-arrow causal relationship given above would be written in terms of deviations of X and Y about their means (i.e., x's and y's) as:

$$x_i = u_{1i}$$
$$(i = 1, \ldots, N)$$
$$a_{21}x_i + y_i = u_{2i} \qquad (6.3)$$

Equations (6.3) are written so that in the first one, x is clearly independent and in the second y is the dependent variable. In the second equation, the coefficient of x (a_{21}) has a subscript corresponding to the location of the off-diagonal asterisk in the matrix above. Both u's represent residual or error terms; note how one u is given for each variable.

For a direct causal relation between x and y, what assumptions must be made? There are only two: corresponding to Lazarsfeld's "substantive ordering," requirement, x is *supposed to precede y.* This is why a_{12}, which does not appear in Equation (6.3), is zero. Secondly, *residual error terms are assumed to be uncorrelated with each other.* The uncorrelated errors assumption assures that there is no prior variable C affecting *both* X and Y. For if this were so, C would be part of u_1 and u_{21} which would then be correlated with each other. In Lazarfeld's terms, partialling out C would also reduce r_{xy} or cause it to vanish. (For further details, see Equation 6.19 below.)

Given these two explicit assumptions, Simon is able to derive a mathematical characteristic of two-variable causal relationships. Basically his method is to multiply together the two equations in (6.3).

$$a_{21}x_i^2 + x_iy_i = u_{1i}u_{2i} \qquad (i = 1, \ldots, N) \qquad (6.4)$$

Now, because x_i and y_i are defined as deviations from their means, so must be the u_1's and u_2's. Therefore the assumption of uncorrelated error terms means that the average standardized product of u_1's and u_2's is zero:

$$r_{u_1 u_2} = \frac{1}{N} \sum_{i=1}^{N} \frac{u_{1i} u_{2i}}{s_{u_1} s_{u_2}} = 0$$

Simplifying, it is clear that requiring residual correlations to be zero is equivalent to asking that covariances and covariations of u_1 and u_2 be zero. In other words, Simon's second assumption requires that

$$\sum_{i=1}^{N} u_{1i} u_{2i} = 0 \tag{6.5}$$

Summing the equations in (6.4), this means that

$$a_{21} \sum x_i^2 + \sum x_i y_i = \sum u_{1i} u_{2i} = 0$$

Solving for a_{21},

$$a_{21} = - \frac{\sum x_i y_i}{\sum x_i^2} = - \frac{s_x}{s_y} r_{yx} \tag{6.6}$$

it follows that the slope a_{21} of Equation (6.3) will be zero or non-zero in exactly the same situations where r_{YX} is zero or non-zero. "*Hence correlation is proof of causation in the two-variable case if we are willing to make the assumptions of time precedence [of X before Y] and non-correlation of the error terms [in Equations 6.3].*"[8]

THREE-VARIABLE CAUSAL RELATIONSHIPS. Three-variable causal models are ones in which relations among theoretical variables X, Y, and Z are postulated and then other variables are assumed not to have any effect on the causal model. By taking the causal effect of a control variable explicitly into account, they are a substantial improvement on two-variable models. Can one use algebraic relationships like those above to deduce distinctive characteristics of three-variable causal theories? Simon argues that the answer is Yes *if* we are willing to make enough *a priori* assumptions.

For a causal system to have only three variables does not mean that no other variables will correlate with x, y, and z. It does mean, however, that variables correlating with, say, x will not *also* correlate with y and z, once their causal relations between x, y, and z have been taken

---

[8] H. Simon, "Spurious Correlation: a Causal Interpretation," *op. cit.*, pp. 42–43. Italics in the original. If we estimate linear mechanisms using regression techniques it is possible also to *tentatively* use these coefficients in testing earlier or making later predictions.

into account. This results in Simon's criteria that residual error terms u_1, u_2, and u_3 will not correlate *with each other:*

$$\sum u_1 u_2 = \sum u_2 u_3 = \sum u_1 u_3 = 0 \qquad (6.7)$$

These equations make explicit the assumptions that theoretical relationships between x, y, and z are valid, "controlling for," "holding constant," or "assuming to be random" the effects of all other variables. Assumptions about the ability of the investigator somehow to isolate subsystems of variables from a complex environment are crucial for making causal inferences in both experimental and nonexperimental natural and social science.

The problem remains of making a sufficiently large number of additional substantive assumptions for determining unique characteristics of any particular three-variable causal model. It is at this point that Lazarsfeld's definition is not sufficiently explicit. Consider the system of linear causal mechanisms between x, y, and z when they are all *interdependent* on each other. In other words, x depends on y and z, y depends on x and z, and z depends on x and y. Using causal arrows, this situation can be succinctly represented:

$$X \rightleftarrows Y$$
$$\nwarrow \searrow \nearrow \swarrow$$
$$Z$$

In a matrix formulation, three-variable interdependence means all diagonal and off-diagonal entries are asterisked:

Variable that influences

		X	Y	Z
	X	*	*	*
Variable being influenced	Y	*	*	*
	Z	*	*	*

The appropriate system of equations again uses x's, y's, and z's taken about their means:

$$x_{21} + a_{12}y_i + a_{13}z_i = u_{1i}$$
$$a_{21}x_i + \quad y_i + a_{23}z_i = u_{2i}$$
$$a_{31}x_i + a_{32}y_i + \quad z_i = u_{3i} \qquad (i = 1, \ldots, N) \qquad (6.8)$$

There are $3 \cdot N$ values of x, y, and z that will be known in N observations. Because we have not ascertained the $3 \cdot N$ values of the residual u's, nor of the a coefficients, however, there are $(3N + 6)$ unknowns, six more than the known information. In order to solve for these six coefficients, Simon argues that we need six *a priori* assumptions for the system (6.8) to have a unique solution, and seven assumptions before specific additional mathematical relations among x, y, and z can be deduced from the causal model.[9]

Assuming the error terms to be uncorrelated [as in Equation (6.7)] produces three of the required additional equations. Theoretical reasoning about the possible orderings of the variables is necessary to determine additional information (a single temporal ordering is not enough). Specifically, it is necessary before any investigation to say why 3 or 4 off-diagonal coefficients *must* be zero. Mathematically, we can then derive useful properties of the causal model that *must* be true if the model and its assumptions are actually correct.

Conventionally, we shall *assume* that y is a dependent variable that influences neither x or z. This means that a_{12} and a_{32} in the system of equations in (6.8) must be zero. The remaining causal possibilities are

$$x \underset{\leftarrow}{\rightrightarrows} z$$
$$\searrow \swarrow$$
$$y \qquad\qquad (6.9)$$

If we also explicitly rule out two-way (reciprocal) causation, this further assumption gives a three-arrow case like

$$x \rightarrow z \qquad\qquad x \leftarrow z$$
$$\searrow \swarrow \quad \text{or} \quad \searrow \swarrow$$
$$y \qquad\qquad y \qquad\qquad (6.10)$$

Having stated the required six additional assumptions, unique values of the coefficients in (6.8) may be obtained. Additional characteristics of the models in (6.10) can best be described, however, *after* the discriminating properties of two-arrow, three-variable causal models have been derived.

Allowing y as only a dependent variable and insisting that at least one more causal arrow in (6.10) does not exist, leaves only five generally possible three-variable causal systems. By putting variables with causal precedence *above* the others, their arrow diagrams and equivalent

---

[9] This argument in "equation-counting" terms should be familiar from high school algebra. It takes two independent equations to solve for two unknowns, three to solve for three, and so forth. The only danger is that one of the equations is not independent of the others and can be derived from them; in this case the number of actual independent equations has to be reduced by one.

linear mechanisms are given in Table 6.2. Each case has been named according to its most salient characteristics, some of which have already been discussed.

What predictions follow from the various assumptions associated with each of these causal models? We shall derive three of the predictions given in Table 6.2, leaving the remaining two cases, double effects and intervening sequences, as exercises for the reader. As the arrow diagrams should make clear, their properties are essentially the same as spurious correlations and developmental sequences, once the appropriate variable labels have been interchanged.

1. *Double causation*. Lazarsfeld's approach corresponds very closely to Simon's direct two-variable causal relationship, but it does not establish how multiple causation should be handled. Therefore, using Simon's methods, let us assume that both x and z cause y,[10] and that

Table 6.2. **Two-arrow, three-variable causal relationships between** x, z, **and a dependent variable** y. **(Error terms are assumed uncorrelated and reciprocal correlation is not allowed.)**

	Description	Diagram	Linear Mechanisms	Predictions
1.	Double cause	$x \quad z$ $\searrow \swarrow$ y	$x \qquad\qquad = u_1$ $a_{21}x + y + a_{23}z = u_2$ $z = u_3$	If $r_{zy} \neq 0$ and $r_{xy} \neq 0$, then $r_{xz} = 0$
2.	Developmental sequence	z $\downarrow$ x $\downarrow$ y	$x \qquad + a_{13}z = u_1$ $a_{21}x + y \qquad = u_2$ $z = u_3$	If $r_{zx} \neq 0$, and $r_{xy} \neq 0$, then $r_{zy} = r_{zx} \cdot r_{xy}$
3.	Double effect	x $\swarrow \searrow$ $y \qquad z$	$x \qquad\qquad = u_1$ $a_{21}x + y \qquad = u_2$ $a_{31}x \qquad + z = u_3$	If $r_{xy} \neq 0$ and $r_{xz} \neq 0$, then $r_{yz} = r_{xy} \cdot r_{xz}$
4.	Spurious correlation	z $\swarrow \searrow$ $x \qquad y$	$x \qquad + a_{13}z = u_1$ $y + a_{23}z = u_2$ $z = u_3$	If $r_{zx} \neq 0$ and $r_{zy} \neq 0$, then $r_{xy} = r_{zx} \cdot r_{zy}$
5.	Intervening sequence	x $\downarrow$ z $\downarrow$ y	$x \qquad\qquad = u_1$ $y + a_{23}z = u_2$ $a_{31}x \qquad + z = u_3$	If $r_{xz} \neq 0$, $r_{zy} \neq 0$, then $r_{xy} = r_{xz} \cdot r_{zy}$

Source: Derivations in the text.

[10] It would be possible for an undetected fourth variable w, uncorrelated with x or z, to be an additional cause of y unless this double causation assumption is made.

the random elements associated with x, y, and z are themselves un-correlated. First, it follows logically from these assumptions that all coefficients not listed in the first set of equations of Table 6.2 are zero, but that a_{21} and a_{23} are not (thus assuring some correlation between x and y and z and y). In addition to these substantive orderings, we are assuming isolated three-variable causal systems, implying that correlations among error terms will be 0:

$$\sum u_1 u_2 = \sum u_1 u_3 = \sum u_{12} = 0 \qquad (6.11)$$

As in the two-variable case, Simon multiplies and sums the linear mechanisms that are assumed to hold for x, z, and y (see Table 6.2). Calculations will be considerably simplified, however, if we first assume that x, y, and z are *standard scores*, with zero means and unit standard deviations. Transforming variables in this way in no way contradicts our assumptions or derivations because equivalent operations on non-standardized variables can always be performed and the final results can be restated in non-standardized terms, if desired.

Equations (6.11) and the causal system in Table 6.2 thus imply that

$$a_{21}\sum x^2 + \sum xy + a_{23}\sum xz = \sum u_1 u_2 = 0$$
$$a_{21}\sum xz + \sum yz + a_{23}\sum z^2 = \sum u_2 u_3 = 0 \qquad (6.12)$$
$$\sum xz = \sum u_1 u_3 = 0$$

The next step is to divide these equations by N in the hope of getting simpler results. Because x's, y's, and z's have been standardized, it follows that their variances (e.g., $\sum z^2/N$) equal one; by a definition of correlation coefficient (as an average cross-product of standardized variables), it also follows logically that cross-products like $\sum xz/N$ are correlation coefficients:

$$a_{21} + r_{xy} + a_{23}r_{xz} = 0$$
$$a_{21} + r_{yz} + a_{23} = 0 \qquad (6.13)$$
$$r_{xz} = 0$$

These results express the relevant linear coefficients in terms of observable correlations [e.g., $a_{23} = (r_{yz} - r_{xy})/(r_{xz} - 1)$]; but, what is more, they tell us that *true double causation models will have uncorrelated independent variables* (here, x and z).

2. *Developmental sequences.* What about the case when an antecedent variable z is involved in a developmental sequence of the form $z \rightarrow x \rightarrow y$? Simon's method actually allows us to distinguish this kind of three-variable relationship from double cause and spurious

correlation models. In particular, legitimate developmental sequences will have different linear mechanisms, with different mathematical properties from spurious models. Using Table 6.2 and Equations (6.11)

$$\sum xz + a_{13}\sum z^2 = \sum u_1 u_3 = 0$$
$$a_{22}\sum xz + \sum yz = \sum u_2 u_3 = 0 \qquad (6.14)$$
$$a_{22}\sum x^2 + \sum xy + a_{13}a_{22}\sum xz + a_{13}\sum yz = \sum u_1 u_2 = 0$$

Dividing by N, these reduce to

$$r_{zx} + a_{13} = 0$$
$$a_{21}r_{zx} + r_{zy} = 0 \qquad (6.15)$$
$$a_{22} + r_{xy} + a_{13}a_{22}r_{zx} + a_{13}r_{zy} = 0$$

The results in Equations (6.15) show first that r_{zx} will be zero only when a_{13} is zero (which would contradict the original assumptions about the nature of developmental sequences); similarly, the assumption of a non-zero a_{21} in the developmental model implies that r_{zy} also could not be zero. Finally, substituting these values of a_{13} and a_{21} into the last equation of (6.15), and simplifying,

$$-\frac{r_{zy}}{r_{zx}} + r_{xy} + r_{zy}r_{zx} - r_{zx}r_{zy} = 0$$

or
$$r_{zy} = r_{xy} \cdot r_{zx} \qquad (6.16)$$

Thus we conclude that *in three-variable development sequences r_{zy} must equal a product of correlations for the intermediate links in the causal chain.*

3. *Spurious correlation.* What can we predict of spurious relationships between x and y caused by a third variable z? Assuming error terms to be uncorrelated, the causal system in Table 6.2 will enjoy the following relationships:

$$\sum xz + a_{13}\sum z^2 = \sum u_1 u_3 = 0$$
$$\sum yz + a_{23}\sum z^2 = \sum u_2 u_3 = 0 \qquad (6.17)$$
$$\sum xy + a_{23}\sum xz + a_{13}\sum yz + a_{13}a_{23}\sum z^2 = \sum u_1 u_2 = 0$$

Dividing by N, substituting values for a_{13} and a_{23}, we have

$$r_{xy} - r_{zy}r_{zx} - r_{zx} + r_{zx}r_{zy} = 0$$

or
$$r_{xy} = r_{zy}r_{zx} \qquad (6.18)$$

Thus we find that in a spurious causation model *the original spurious correlation between x and y will equal a product of correlations between the cause z, x and y.* This result is quite analogous to Lazarsfeld's two-variable result that the individual correlation would equal the marginal product: r_{xy} equals the product of r_{zy} times r_{zx}.

SUMMARY. Before applying Simon's approach in a practical situation, let us summarize some of the implications of his results.

1. Simon derives mathematical properties of different theoretically suggested causal relationships. These properties belong to the models and not (necessarily) to the real world. The logical certainty of his results does not, therefore, extend to empirical reality and does not violate Hume's contention that all we *observe* are covariations. Applying these models to empirical observations will give results which are at best tentative because the theoretical elimination of certain causal arrows may be shown to be invalid and because the *a priori* mathematical *assumptions of uncorrelated error terms and the number of relevant variables can always be proved wrong at some future date by the poor fit of model predictions with actual data.*

2. Several different causal models make the same predictions: spurious, correlation sequences and intervening sequences, for example, both predict that $r_{xy} = r_{xz} \cdot r_{yz}$. Developmental sequences and those in which x has a "double effect" on both y and z also yield similar confusions (see Table 6.2). *Several simple four- and five-variable models also are consistent with each of these possibilities.* These examples make clear that several *a priori* substantive orderings of variables will be tested in an empirical assessment, unless all other models making identical predictions can be theoretically or empirically eliminated beforehand by some other means. This is especially true when model coefficients (the a's) are not predicted ahead of time. The more likely empirical approach will be to proceed by eliminating certain classes of causal models and failing to eliminate others.

3. For the five two-arrow models of causal relationships three distinct *classes* of results are predicted by Simon's method. With y as a dependent variable only, and disallowing reciprocal causation (arrows like $\rightleftarrows$), Simon's method can distinguish (1) double causes from (2) developmental sequences and double effects, and (3) spurious correlations and intervening sequences. By elimination, that is, whenever we know that none of these predictions are born out for a three-variable causal system, it is possible to deduce that three-arrow relationships actually exist [such as those in Equations (6.8)]. To distinguish between two different possible *three*-arrow relationships, however, additional substantive orderings need to be established.

4. Simon's results can be summarized by using partial correlation coefficients. These coefficients are completely analogous to the condi-

tional (within group) covariance coefficients defined in Chapter 5. They represent the correlation between two variables when the effect of a third variable on each has already been removed or controlled for. The partial correlation coefficient between variables 1 and 2, controlling for 3, $(r_{12.3})$ is given by the formula:

$$r_{12.3} = \frac{r_{12} - r_{13}r_{23}}{\sqrt{1 - r_{13}^2}\,\sqrt{1 - r_{23}^2}} \qquad (6.19)^{11}$$

Whenever $r_{12.3} = 0$, $r_{12} = r_{13} \cdot r_{23}$, and *vice versa*. Thus *for both developmental sequences and double effects, $r_{zy.x} = 0$; and for spurious relations and intervening sequences between x and y, $r_{xy.z} = 0$.* Double causes will give simple correlations equal to zero, while three-arrow relationships will make neither simple nor partial correlations disappear.

5. Although we have not shown so here, Simon has shown that these predictions about correlations are *necessary* and *sufficient* conditions for the specified coefficients in the related linear mechanism to vanish (see Table 6.2). Thus, when there is no problem of measurement or sampling error, and the *a priori* assumptions of a two-arrow three-variable causal model can at least partly be justified, the correct class of causal models can tentatively be chosen by looking at individual and partial correlations.

6. Most importantly, Simon's method generalizes to many-variable cases *without* too much difficulty in many cases. The more theoretical assumptions about certain mechanism coefficients being zero that can be justified, the more predictions will be made from which particular many-variable models can be chosen.

C.   A Provisional Causal Analysis

There is a growing body of literature in economics, political science, and sociology applying Simon's interpretations of causal relationships. Some of the most exciting results have been regarding four- and five-variable models of social change.[12] Causal laws, after all, are the best possible way of describing historical trends and predicting or projecting

---

[11] In other words, $r_{12.3}$ is the correlation of the residuals from linear regressions of variables 1 and 2 on variable 3. Rewriting (6.19) as

$$r_{12} = \sqrt{1 - r_{13}^2}\,\sqrt{1 - r_{23}^2}\,r_{12.3} + r_{13}r_{23}$$

should recall the form of Theorem 5.1, the covariance theorem.

[12] Blalock's *Causal Inference in Nonexperimental Research, op. cit.*, discusses several results for four- and five-variable examples.

future developments. As we saw in Chapter 2, these are two of the main tasks of political analysis.

Working from aggregate data, we shall limit ourselves in this context to testing some plausible two-arrow, three-variable causal models whose mathematical characteristics have already been developed and are summarized in Table 6.2. Because two, four, five, and larger variable models have not also been tried, tentative results are more likely to illustrate the *kinds* of decisions the Simon method allows rather than to indicate definitive conclusions.

CAUSES AND EFFECTS OF NEGRO VOTING STRENGTH. Several important arguments about the influence and power of Negro and white political activity on each other have been advanced. Three of these, here labeled the "white oppression theory," the "Uncle Tom theory," and the "Ku Klux Klan theory," will be briefly outlined and then subjected to a provisional empirical test.

The variables from which these (simplified) theories have been constructed are Negro voting strength, white race organizations, and white racial discontent. Total Negro voting registrations have been divided by white registration figures for each of more than 300 Southern counties. The resulting ratio (symbolized N/WR) has been used as an index of Negro voting strength. Anti-Negro racial feeling has been measured, for simplicity, by a single index, the percentage of States Rights voting in the 1948 election ($SR48$). The existence of white racist organizations (WRO) was coded as a dichotomous 0 or 1 dummy variable.[13]

The oppression theory held by many Negroes and Northerners considers both white anti-Negro feeling and the efforts of white racist organizations to be the causes of restrictions on Negro voting registration and Negro voting strength. Although an oversimplified view (the effects of education, Negro population concentrations, and urbanization probably should not be considered random), the kernel of this theory is at least plausible.

Uncle Tom theories of Negro political behavior suggest that if the Negro kept in his place (in the pantry or in the fields) and did not agi-

[13] Correlations between Negro/White Registration Ratios, national vote for the States Rights Party in 1948, and the existence of white racial organizations were calculated for data from 311 counties in Texas, Alabama, and Arkansas. The relevant information has kindly been made available to the author by Donald N. Mathews and James W. Prothro. See their "Social and Economic Factors and Negro Voter Registration in the South," *American Political Science Review*, **58**, 1 (March 1963), pp. 24–44; and their "Political Factors and Negro Voter Registration in the South," *American Political Science Review*, **58**, 2 (June 1963), pp. 355–367.

tate for political power, racist organizations and anti-Negro prejudice would not occur. The role of Northern agitators is also usually mentioned. Rather than predict that white sentiments and organizations *decrease* Negro registrations, the Uncle Tom theory hypothesizes just the opposite: increased Negro activity *increases* the white response.

Finally, an often mentioned "power elite" theory is that the white racist organizations (especially the Ku Klux Klan) have stirred up anti-Negro prejudice that was previously latent or did not exist. This prejudice then explains the restrictions on Negro voting registrations. This theory, at least to some, also has considerable plausibility.

TESTING THE THEORIES. Although the above descriptions are little more than caricatures of various points of view (two- or three-variable theories usually are), they provide enough assumptions about the orderings among the three variables for the theories to be tested, *if* one further set of assumptions can be made. These further assumptions state that the relevant error terms are uncorrelated. As suggested in each of the theories just outlined, other recognizable causal variables *are* involved. These uncorrelated error assumptions *at best* mean that these additional effects are considerably smaller than the others already taken into account (see Table 6.3).

A further reservation that should be mentioned has to do with the validity and reliability of the indices being used. Dividing Negro and white registrations by their respective population sizes might have improved the index of Negro voting strength. Using States' Rights voting at the county level must be admitted as an inaccurate indicator of anti-Negro prejudice at best. It is an ecological variable, collected ten years before the rest of the data; other indices (like anti-Negro riots, speeches, opinions) would help make a more valid and reliable index. For all three variables, measurement error might further have reduced the reliabilities. Finally, the inherently ecological nature of the data must be stressed. Findings about county political systems are all that can legitimately be inferred.

Even with these reservations in mind, the three models summarized in Table 6.3 appear to be confirmed to the same extent as the subjective plausibilities suggested above. The prediction of the oppression theory fits the actual results fairly well. But other variables do indeed seem to be involved. Secondly, the Uncle Tom theory, although giving a closer fit, is disastrously wrong. As worded above, Negro agitations (registrations) were supposed to increase white racist responses in the various counties being studied. The signs of the correlations, however, are both quite highly *negative*, indicating that only a reversed Uncle

Table 6.3. **The Causes and Consequences of Negro Voting Strength: Relations among anti-Negro feeling (States' Rights voting in 1948 [SR48]), Negro voting strength ([Negro/White registration ratio [N/WR]) and the existence of white racist organizations (WRO).**

1. Oppression Theory

Model	Prediction	Result	Decision
WRO(X) `⋅42` `⋅53` N/WR(Y) SR48(Z)	$r_{zz} = 0$	0.15	Fit is fair, cannot completely reject

2. Uncle Tom Theory

Model	Prediction	Result	Decision
`⋅42` WRO(X) N/WR(Y) `⋅53` SR48(Z)	$r_{zz} = 0.22$	0.15	Closer fit, but from opposite signs; restate or reject

3. Ku Klux Klan Theory

Model	Prediction	Result	Decision
`⋅15` SR48(Z) WRO(X) `⋅53` N/WR(Y)	$r_{xy} = -0.08$	-0.42	Fit is quite poor, reject even though plausible originally

Tom theory makes any sense (i.e., increased Negro registrations will *decrease* white racist resistance). Perhaps because of the effects of urbanism and higher education such results may occur (an unexpectedly gratifying and new hypothesis).

Finally, the Ku Klux Klan elite theory gives a substantially worse fit than the oppression theory discussed above. The relationship between white racist organizations and States Rights' voting (a poor index) is much too small. At best the elitist organization theory has only a small hint of the truth when comparing counties as political units.

CONCLUSION. Causal arguments are highly controversial and need more valid operational indicators than those given above; they also require more systematic examination of other possible non-random influences on pairs of residual terms. Nonetheless, when parsimonious theories are stated in "other things being equal" or "random" terms, they are susceptible to decisive mathematical investigation. Multivariate quantitative methods for stating and testing causal empirical political hypotheses can make a highly useful contribution to political analysis.

CHAPTER 7

Strategy, Morality, and Politics

> *... It may safely be stated that there exists, at present, no satisfactory treatment of the question of rational behavior.*
>
> VON NEUMANN AND MORGENSTERN

ALTHOUGH SOME RELATED PROBLEMS remain highly controversial, twentieth-century mathematics has progressed remarkably toward mathematically characterizing rational competitive and cooperative behavior. Many of their results have emanated from von Neumann and Morgenstern's classic *Theory of Games and Economic Behavior*.[1] Since longer introductions to game theory exist elsewhere,[2] we shall limit ourselves to presenting and discussing some of the basic results in this area and commenting on their relevance to political analysis.

At the outset an important caveat is necessary:

[It] is crucial that the social scientist recognize that game theory is not [necessarily] *descriptive* but rather (conditionally) *normative*. It states neither how people do behave nor how they should behave in an absolute sense, but how they should behave if they wish to achieve certain ends. It prescribes for given assumptions causes of action for the attainment of outcomes having certain formal "optimum" properties. These properties may or may not be deemed pertinent in any given real world conflict of interest. If they are, the theory prescribes the choices which *must* be made to get that optimum.[3]

---

[1] Princeton University Press, 1944.

[2] Two excellent 100-page introductions to the subject relevant to political analysis are "Part II: The Logic of Strategy," in Anatol Rapoport's *Fights, Games and Debates* (Ann Arbor: University of Michigan Press, 1960), and "Game Theory and the Study of Social Behavior: An Introductory Exposition," in Martin Shubik (ed.), *Game Theory and Related Approaches to Social Behavior* (New York: Wiley, 1964). The best critical, book-length exposition of the theory and related literature is R. Duncan Luce and Howard Raiffa, *Games and Decisions* (New York: Wiley, 1957). None of these treatments relies heavily on advanced mathematics.

[3] Luce and Raiffa, *op. cit.*, p. 63. Italics in the original. Most of the terms and game theory results in this chapter are reported in Luce and Raiffa, Chapters 4, 5, and 14.

A.   Zero-sum Rationality in Conflict Situations

Game theory talks mathematically about conflicts of interests.   It confronts competing, rational players with one another in choice situations and determines strategies that maximize (in various ways) their value outcomes.   The values (called utilities) that they attach to alternative outcomes are measured on interval scales, and perfect information about the other players' utilities is also assumed.   We shall first consider conflict situations where the utilities of two players are completely opposed, so that, what one player gets, another loses.   These conflicts are called two-person zero-sum games.

TWO-PERSON ZERO-SUM GAMES.   Consider the following hypothetical example.   Two players, Jack and Jill, are competing for presidency of the senior class.   As candidates they have only two feasible campaign issues: their sex differences or the need for good government.   Speeches about masculine or feminine superiority would fall into the first category; promises about improving the work of the student council would be good government strategies.

What are the payoffs of the various campaign strategies?   In game theory terms, this means determining the utilities of various outcomes for each player.   We shall assume (perhaps unrealistically) that they aspire to post-election advantages of public commitments in the candidate's favor from the four leading campus fraternities.   How many of these will have announced in a candidate's behalf will depend on the campaign tactics each pursues.   Let us even assume that both Jack and Jill have complete information about the utility outcomes of each conjunction of strategies.   Hypothetical payoffs are summarized in Table 7.1, where each cell entry contains two numbers: first the net support for Jack, then the net support for Jill.   From Table 7.1 we see that Jack would do extremely well in a battle of the sexes.   He would win 4 fraternities' support while Jill would have 4 come out against her, an unhappy outcome for her with a utility of -4.   (Note how in a zero-sum game the utilities in each cell of the payoff matrix add to zero.)   But if Jill *knew* that Jack was going to emphasize sex differences, she would be foolish to do so herself.   In fact, her biggest payoff would occur if she emphasized good government and Jack did, too.   She would get two endorsements, and Jack would get none (in effect, -2, since two fraternities had come out against him).

Once the possible outcomes have been listed and their values determined (i.e., the utility of each outcome to both candidates), game

Table 7.1. **Payoff matrix for a hypothetical two-person zero-sum contest for the senior class presidency.**

		Jill campaign strategies	
Campaign strategies		sex issue	good government
Jack	sex issue	(4, −4)	(1, −1)
	good government	(3, −3)	(−2, 2)

theory shows mathematically how certain general rules for maximizing utility correspond to specific choices of strategies. For zero-sum situations, game theorists have defined maximizing rationality either in an optimistic or a pessimistic manner: let the *security level of a single strategy be the smallest guaranteed utility* associated with choosing that alternative. Then, for Jack and Jill, *zero-sum rationality* means

(1) either optimistically maximizing his (or her) security level;

(2) or pessimistically minimizing the effects of the opponent's security maximizing strategy.

Strategies that maximize one's own guaranteed minimum utility are called *maximin strategies;* those minimizing an opponent's maximum security level are called *minimax strategies.*

Do single maximin strategies exist for Jack and Jill? Do they at the same time also minimax the impact of the other's best attack? In Table 7.1, Jack can *guarantee* a net advantage of one support unit by speaking only about the sex of the other candidate. Jill can maximize her security level by talking only about the good government. In this way would both players also minimize the guaranteed gains of their opponent? In our example, the answer is yes. Jack would very much like to talk about masculine superiority. The best that Jill can do to neutralize his efforts is to campaign on another issue. Similarly, Jack can minimize Jill's security level by counteracting her good government campaign with allusions to her femininity. This finding suggests an important property of the payoff matrix in Table 7.1: *for each player maximin and minimax strategies coincide.*

Zero-sum rationality can thus be defined in either maximin or minimax terms. In the above example both players' assumptions that their opponent would do the best he could to minimize their gains and maximize their losses led to a *strictly determined solution* of the senior president example: There is a particular cell entry (the upper right corner of Table 7.1) which is *simultaneously the minimum of the row in which it occurs and the maximum of its column.* From a geometric analog for a whole series of alternatives, this point is called a saddle-point. Against a malicious opponent neither player can with certainty do better than the utilities obtained in that particular cell. The size of this cell entry for the row contestant V is called the *value of the game*, in our example, 1. Jack's *optimal* strategy is to pick the row containing V; Jill also can do no better than to choose the column where V and $-V$ appear. It would be appropriate in this case to say that, when V is bigger than zero, Jack has more potential influence or power than Jill. He expects to get a higher reward no matter what strategy she tries.

THE MINIMAX THEOREM. Some zero-sum games, even in the simple 2×2 matrix form of Table 7.1, do not have saddlepoints and strictly determined solutions. In such games, *single-choice* minimax and maximin strategies do not coincide for either player, endangering the attractive coincidence of these alternate ways of defining zero-sum rationality.[4]

Consider Table 7.2. Party candidates D and R are competing in a national election, in which they can emphasize either foreign or domestic issues. We shall assume that the utility of the outcomes for each

Table 7.2. **Payoff matrix for a hypothetical zero-sum presidential contest.**

		Strategies of Republican Candidate (R)	
		Domestic Issues	*Foreign Issues*
Strategies of Democratic Candidate (D)	Domestic Issues	$(3, -3)$	$(-2, 2)$
	Foreign Issues	$(-1, 1)$	$(2, -2)$

[4] All payoff matrices for non-strictly determined 2×2 zero-sum games can be symbolized in either of two ways:

$$\begin{array}{cc} a_{11} > a_{12} \\ \vee \quad \wedge \\ a_{21} < a_{22} \end{array} \quad \text{or} \quad \begin{array}{cc} a_{11} < a_{12} \\ \wedge \quad \vee \\ a_{21} > a_{22} \end{array}$$

In these situations, there is no row minimum which is also a column maximum. For more details see Chapter 6 of John G. Kemeny, J. Laurie Snell, and Gerald L. Thompson, *Introduction to Finite Mathematics* (Englewood Cliffs, N.J.: Prentice-Hall, 1957).

candidate have been computed, are known to each, and have opposite signs so that the election game is again *zero-sum*. (Empirically, of course, these assumptions would at best be approximations: utilities would not be known with certainty, even by one of the candidates, better information might be too costly to obtain, and payoffs might change over time.)

The dilemma of Table 7.2 is that zero-sum rationality seems no longer defined. The Democrat finds his maximum security in foreign affairs (he can lose at most by one utility unit), but this maximum of his minima is no longer impregnable to his opponent's most malicious intent. The Republican, for example, will be much better off, once he knows the Democrat is emphasizing foreign issues, by himself talking exclusively about domestic concerns. But, if the Democrat knows the Republican will be domestically oriented, he, too, would change to the same kind of concern and be able to defeat his opponent handsomely; but then the Republican would . . . , etc., etc. *It is no longer possible with a single strategy to maximize his own security level while at the same time guaranteeing that his opponent's gains will be minimized.*

Von Neumann's great contribution was to reestablish the meaning of zero-sum rationality in non-strictly determined games. He did this by introducing the possibility of "mixed strategies," and "expected utilities" attached to them. A mixed strategy is exactly as it sounds. Rather than playing one choice (e.g., emphasizing *only* domestic issues), it means being willing to make any of several moves, each according to a specific probability. In playing repeated Presidential games (one per month), a mixed strategy might be to emphasize foreign affairs *half* the months and domestic affairs the rest. For a one-shot game, a 50–50 mixed strategy would be to flip an unbiased coin and then talk about domestic affairs if it comes up heads, or *vice versa*. Von Neumann introduces the random element to minimize the opponent's certainty of what choice will be made in any particular move. The reasonable idea is that of emphasizing one's good points without altogether ignoring the various possible responses by the other candidate.

Expected utilities of mixed strategies can be calculated in the same actuarial way used by insurance companies. In determining the "expected cost" of a policy, they multiply probabilities of death at each age level times the cost to them of death at that age and then sum these products to get an expected cost. If probabilities of dying remain constant or improve, *in the long run*, they can expect an overall profit by charging more than the "expected cost" of the policy. Similarly in Table 7.2, the expected value of *D*'s choosing either emphasis with a

50–50 chance can be calculated as soon as the probabilities of each kind of move by the other player is known.[5]

Using these concepts of mixed strategies and expected payoffs, von Neumann is able to reestablish the meaningfulness of minimax-maximin zero-sum rationality in a way that determines optimal strategies for each player in the following theorem:

The Minimax Theorem: For any zero-sum two person game with a finite number of strategy alternatives for players D and R, there exists a number V, a maximin strategy for player D which guarantees him an expected utility of at least V, and a minimax strategy for player R which guarantees that player D gets an expected utility of at most V, provided that both D and R are allowed probabilistically to mix their various strategy alternatives.[6]

COMMENT. Von Neumann's theorem, whose proof is fairly complicated and therefore will not be given here, is a classic mathematical tautology of relevance to the social sciences. It is a piece of mathematics created for describing competitive human behavior. In one sense, all it does is to give a logically consistent redefinition of the principle of zero-sum rationality which, when approximately valid, can be applied to certain political situations.[7] In the hypothetical example of Table 7.2 the theory asserts that the most "rational" strategy that D can choose in this zero-sum situation is a *combination* of foreign and domestic references. Using the correct computational formulas, we discover that the "best" strategy for the Democratic candidate is to spend only 3/8 of his time on his "best" issue, domestic

[5] The von Neumann-Morgenstern theory calculates interval measures of utility in a similar way. Consider a slightly different example from the one in the text above. A Northern liberal Democrat most prefers Stevenson as President (arbitrarily give this outcome a utility value of 100) and least desires Senator Goldwater (give this outcome a utility value of 0, thereby determining an interval scale). How much utility does he attach to Lyndon Johnson's Presidency? To answer this question, we confront him with a series of choices. That is, we find from him the probability mixture of getting Stevenson or Goldwater, the expected value of which would just equal the value of a certain Johnson election. In economic language, we find the point of indifference between these alternatives. (Ask questions like: "Would you prefer Johnson for sure to a mixed situation in which Adlai had a 90 percent chance of being elected over Goldwater? 85 percent? etc.") Johnson's utility to the Northerner would equal 100 times the probability of getting Stevenson plus 0 times the probability of getting Goldwater, at the point where he equally preferred the certainty of having Johnson elected to getting the mixed package.

[6] This statement combines several elements given in Luce and Raiffa, *op. cit.*, pp. 71–72. Various general methods of solution are given in Appendices 3 to 6 of that book.

[7] William H. Riker, for example, has written *The Theory of Political Coalitions* (New Haven: Yale University Press, 1963) using and reworking N-person zero-sum game theories. His results have a surprisingly wide range of applicability to practical politics.

affairs, certainly not an obvious result. Nor is it obvious that the Republican should divide his time evenly (1/2, 1/2) among domestic and foreign concerns.[8] The strategies can be shown, however, to minimax the opposing candidate's security and to *guarantee* the highest possible expected return, regardless of the nature of opposing strategems. (Try it! Expected utility gains can be computed by summing the probabilities for each alternative times the utility of the alternative.)

Finally, von Neumann establishes a way of calculating the potential influence (i.e., value potential) of either contestant in the non-strictly determined game. What *value* does the game have to player D? Using a minimax strategy, he can expect to recieve a utility of 1/2. Potentially, at least, D can *guarantee* one-half utility unit more than R, whatever counterstrategy R employs.

B.   Cooperative Rationality in Non-zero-sum Conflicts

Non-zero-sum political situations are frequent enough to warrant further hypothetical investigations into the nature of an appropriate concept of rationality.

[8] For cases of two strategy alternatives, Kemeny, Snell, and Thompson, *op. cit.*, p. 276, give the following formulas for optimal mixed strategies. Let the utility payoffs for player D (whose single strategies are different rows in Table 7.2) be represented by a's with natural row and column subscripts:

R

		Strategy 1	Strategy 2
	Strategy 1	a_{11}	a_{12}
D			
	Strategy 2	a_{21}	a_{22}

The optimal mixed strategies for D (d_1^0, d_2^0) and for R (r_1^0, r_2^0), where the superscript 0's refer to the optimal strategy mix, are given by

$$(d_1^0, d_2^0) = \frac{a_{22} - a_{21}}{S}, \quad \frac{a_{11} - a_{12}}{S}$$

$$(r_1^0, r_2^0) = \frac{a_{22} - a_{12}}{S}, \quad \frac{a_{11} - a_{21}}{S}$$

In all these cases $S = a_{11} + a_{22} - a_{12} - a_{21}$, and is obtained by subtracting the sum of diagonal entries in one diagonal from the sum of those in the other. The expected (long-run) value of the game V is determined by seeing what return player D can be expected to receive if he plays his optimal, maximin strategy (d_1^0, d_2^0), and player R plays his minimax strategy (r_1^0, r_2^0). A simplified formula is

$$V = \frac{a_{11}a_{22} - a_{12}a_{21}}{S}$$

Using the payoff matrix in Table 7.2 these formulas give (d_1^0, d_2^0) = ($\frac{3}{8}, \frac{5}{8}$), (r_1^0, r_2^0) = ($\frac{1}{3}, \frac{1}{2}$), and $V = \frac{1}{2}$.

THE PRISONERS' DILEMMA.   Consider the example of a non-zero-sum game known as the prisoners' dilemma given in Table 7.3.[9]   Two prisoners, who have committed a crime together, are separately faced by the district attorney with the alternatives of "squealing" or not "squealing" on one another.   If only one confesses, he will get a very short jail term (less than a year — its utility equals 10) while the other will go to jail for 10 years (utility of 0).   Total utilities in each of these cases are much higher than the "unhappy" result when both confess. If both "squeal," however, they each will get 9 years in jail (a utility of 1 for each, totaling only 2).   Only by both refusing to talk, in which case the district attorney lacks sufficient evidence for major convictions, will they each be able to get off with light sentences—2 years each.

The utilities of the joint "do not confess" strategy sum to 16, much higher than any other combination.   Although zero-sum rationality is thus not necessarily appropriate, let us see what it suggests to each prisoner.   As the district attorney and the law have structured their situation, each is tempted to "squeal" in the hope that the other will not.   Each in a sense also maximizes his own security level by doing so (the worst penalty when one confesses is worth 1, not 0).   Although mixed strategies might alleviate the situation to a small extent, "squealing" also has the advantage (if one is being entirely competitive) of minimizing the other's gains.   But if both are going to "guarantee" themselves 9 years in jail (utilities of 1), the dilemma posed squarely by Table 7.3 is: *why has the chance of only 2-year terms for both become so clearly unobtainable?*

THE ETHICS OF COOPERATION.   The way for the prisoners to reach the rather attractive (but not individually optimal) goal of 2-year terms for each is through prior communication and binding agreements, enforced by sanctions not appearing in the utility matrix of Table 7.3.   Certainly, this is how the Mafia works, with severe outside penalties for those who "squeal," because of the moral obligations and vows of a blood brotherhood.

National societies should be able to do as well as the Mafia in solving the prisoners' dilemma; sometimes they do, and with less cruel consequences for their neighbors.   Game theoretical analyses of bargaining, arbitration, and "fair" divisions of the spoils have made an appreciable

[9] This example is attributed to A. W. Tucker and is discussed by both Luce and Raiffa, *op. cit.*, and Rapoport, *op. cit.* The interested reader can find other analyses of anti-trust law, international law, and cold war accommodation expressed in non-zero-sum terms in Martin Shubik, *Strategy and Market Structure* (New York: Wiley, 1959); Morton Kaplan and Nicholas Katzenbach, *The Political Foundations of International Law* (New York: Wiley, 1961); and A. Rapoport, *Strategy and Conscience* (New York: Harper and Row, 1964).

increment to man's understanding of rational cooperative behavior. In this section we shall briefly comment on one proposed solution to the meaning of rational cooperative behavior, the work of a mathematician and econometrician, John Nash.[10]

In a brilliant analysis, Nash has explicated the concept of rational self-interest in two-person bargaining situations. He presents a solution concept for two-person cooperative games, which, by definition, are

Table 7.3. **The prisoner's dilemma.**

		Prisoner *B* Strategy	
		Confess	*Do not Confess*
Prisoner *A* Strategy	*Confess*	(1, 1)	(10, 0)
	Do not Confess	(0, 10)	(8, 8)

characterized by preplay communication, binding agreements, and non-zero-sum payoff matrices. Nash presents and justifies four component requirements for rational bargaining. They may be discussed with respect to Figure 7.1, which portrays various utility outcomes for *A* and *B* in the prisoners' dilemma. We shall assume that a minimax-maximin approach will assure *A* and *B*, by joint confessions, a (1, 1) utility outcome, and that they have time to discuss their situation and make a firm agreement. We shall assume (reasonably, but without the actual calculations) that any outcome in the prospect space of Figure 7.1 may result from various *degrees of confessions*, a possibility not considered in the previous example. Degrees of confession could presumably be measured by the number of years in jail they would entail.

Let us also assume that Nash is the prisoners' attorney, asked to arbitrate their differences, regardless of their actual guilt, ignoring pos-

[10] R. B. Braithwaite appears to be one of the few professors of philosophy who has taken game theory's normative aspects seriously, and in an entertaining fashion. See his *Theory of Games as a Tool for the Moral Philosopher; An Inaugural Lecture by the Knightsbridge Professor of Moral Philosophy in the University of Cambridge*, (Cambridge: Cambridge University Press, 1955). Braithwaite and many welfare economists depart from Nash on the use of an axiom of the independence of irrelevant alternatives (to be discussed below). For helpful comments and more detailed analysis, see Luce and Raiffa, *op. cit.*, and Rapoport, *op. cit.* Nash's papers on "The Bargaining Problem" and "Two Person Cooperative Games," both appeared in *Econometrica*, **18**, 2 (April 1950), pp. 155–62 and **21**, 1 (January 1953), pp. 128–41 respectively. John Harsanyi has considerably generalized these results: "A Simplified Bargaining Model for the *n*-Person Cooperative Game," *International Economic Review*, **4**, 2 (May 1963), pp. 194–220.

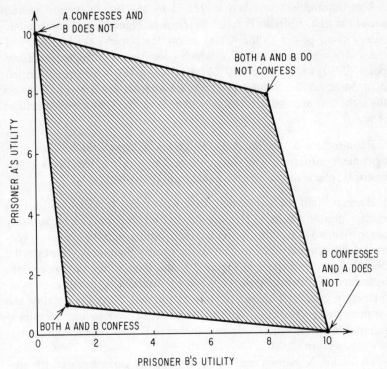

FIGURE 7.1 Prospect space for The Prisoners' Dilemma.
Source: see Table 7.3.

sible consequences not revealed in the jointly perceived payoff possibilities of Table 7.3 or Figure 7.1. He suggests the following.

Requirement 1. (Invariance with respect to utility measurement) Whatever fair solution is recommended must give an equivalent result when the utilities of either prisoner are subjected to linear transformations.

This requirement corresponds to restating the assumption that utilities have been measured on interval scales. Visually, it means that the uniform stretching or movement of the shaded area of prospective bargaining solutions in Figure 7.1 will bring an old "fair solution" into a new one.

Requirement 2. (Joint efficiency or Pareto optimality) Any solution whose only effect is to increase the utilities of one or both players is preferable to one that leaves both utilities the same.

This requirement was first suggested by the Italian economist and social theorist, Vilfredo Pareto. In terms of Figure 7.1, it immediately rules out all points to the left or below the upper right boundary of the utility region in Figure 7.1, which goes from one single confession point (0, 10) to the other (10, 0). For any point below or to the left of a point on this boundary there are alternatives above and/or to the right that are preferred by *A* or *B* or both and that penalize neither *A* nor *B*.

Requirement 3. (Symmetry) Players with equal utilities in a non-agreement situation, and interchangeable utility alternatives (symmetrical roles), should receive equal utility payoffs.

It seems "fair" to require that players in exactly similar situations get exactly similar results. (This assumption involves interpersonal utility comparisons.) In the above example utility alternatives are geometrically symmetrical, so that a line going diagonally through the diamond prospect space in Figure 7.1, and intersecting the upper right boundary of "Pareto points" at (8, 8), contains a number of symmetrically "fair" solutions. In conjunction with Pareto optimality, the symmetry requirement is itself sufficient to produce a unique bargaining solution to the prisoners' dilemma shown in Figure 7.1, i.e., the boundary intersection (8, 8).

To assure the same result when the original game begins with *nonsymmetric sets of utility alternatives*, however, it is necessary to introduce a controversial additional requirement:

Requirement 4. [Independence of irrelevant (unchosen) alternatives] If one set of possible bargain outcomes (called a "prospect space") includes another, and both have the same disagreement solution, then any solution in the larger space will also be a solution to the smaller one, provided only that it is a possible alternative in the smaller game.

This requirement allows any non-symmetric prospect space to be included in a larger symmetric prospect space which has a common solution point. It may be rationalized as saying that bargainers should concern themselves only with improvements over the "no agreement" point (the *status quo* if no bargain is struck) rather than highly attractive possibilities for one but not the other player. For convex, bounded prospect spaces (ones of finite dimensions without any indentations), Nash uses the four requirements to establish an extremely general result:

Nash's Theorem. In convex, bounded prospect spaces including their boundaries, one and only one solution point for a bargaining game can be found which fulfills requirements 1–4. *It is the point at which the* product *of utility differences from the disagreement point is maximized.*

Requirements 1–4 are thus logically equivalent to the simple mathematical rule of solving cooperative two-person non-zero-sum games by multiplying utilities (taken about no agreement points) and picking the point giving the biggest product.[11]

Multiplying $(8 - 1) \times (8 - 1)$ gives 49 in the above example, the highest possible utility product. Therefore Nash's theorem states that the joint non-confession solution to the prisoners' dilemma, if enforceable, is optimally rational from the point of view of the collective interest.

Nash's reasoning suggests a kind of *social contract* between members of a society. By defining "cooperative rationality" in a precise and plausible way, it produces exact solutions to semicompetitive situations and reduces a plausible arbitration scheme to a minimal set of general concepts. In real situations, payoffs will not always be known; nor will "fair" bargains always be struck. The utility of game theory for descriptive and normative purposes in these situations is nonetheless clear. It defines "cooperative rationality" as an "ideal type" (Weber's term) of agreement process in direct contrast to the "zero-sum rationality" concept previously introduced. Behavior can be *described* or *criticized* to the extent it departs from either of these criteria.[12]

C. Game Theory and Democratic Theory

Game theory is more than exhortation. Kenneth Arrow's generalizations of the voters' paradox have stimulated a rethinking of the basic

[11] This result is a beautiful example of how certain reasonable or qualitative considerations lead to a unique and surprising quantitative result. A more explicit proof of this theorem, and a discussion of the merits of assuming the "independence of irrelevant alternatives" may be found in Luce and Raiffa, *op. cit.*, pp. 124–137. The proof follows essentially the course suggested above. Any prospect space is subjected to a linear transformation until its disagreement point is $(0, 0)$ and its point with a maximum utility product is $(1, 1)$. A symmetric prospect space can then be circumscribed about this entire space, intersecting it only at $(1, 1)$. But, as reasoned above, Pareto optimality and symmetry require this point to be a unique solution for a symmetric convex prospect space, and, by the independence of irrelevant alternatives, it is therefore a solution to the original game. The uniqueness of this result and its ability to satisfy all of Nash's requirements can be easily shown.

[12] Anatol Rapoport and his colleagues, for example, have experimentally investigated the social and psychological characteristics of decision-makers that lead to competitive zero-sum behavior or cooperative rationality in situations where the actual payoff matrices are unclear. See, for example, his *Strategy and Conscience*, *op. cit.*, Chapter 14.

assumptions of democratic political and economic theory.[13] Arrow rediscovered a paradox that Condorcet, Nanson, Dodgson (Lewis Carroll), and Black had already found.[14]

THE VOTERS' PARADOX. Consider a hypothetical three-membered society named Threemanland that determines its collective preferences by a 2/3 majority vote. Further allow that these preferences can only be measured with ordinal levels of accuracy. The citizens of Threemanland are trying to choose their form of government (a very old problem in political analysis). They perceive three modern alternatives: capitalistic democracy (labeled "democracy"), democratic socialism (labeled "socialism"), and dictatorial communism ("communism"). Indicating "is preferred to" by ">," the three citizens prefer these alternatives in the following order:

> Citizen 1: democracy > socialism > communism
> Citizen 2: socialism > communism > democracy
> Citizen 3: communism > democracy > socialism

Each of these orderings has some plausibility: Citizen 1 is a "real" democrat; Citizen 2 is a very anti-capitalistic socialist; and Citizen 3 is a red-blooded communist, who hates democratic socialism most of all.

Simply counting preferences, however, leads to the following results. Two citizens (1 and 3) prefer democracy to socialism; two others (1 and 2) prefer socialism to communism; but Citizens 2 and 3 prefer communism to democracy. What has happened to our democratic procedure of majority voting? These three judgments imply that, collectively, the citizenry favors democracy over socialism and socialism over communism. If collective voter preferences are rational, they should be *transitive* (see Chapter 2), from which it naturally follows that they also prefer democracy to communism. But we have just seen how two out of three voters prefer communism to democracy! In this example, then, a 2/3 majority procedure produces "intransitive decisions." Such a result seems a towering example of collective irrationality.

---

[13] Arrow's original work is *Social Choice and Individual Values*, Cowles Commission Monograph 12 (New York: Wiley, 1951). Some of the best thoughts about Arrow's results are in Robert Dahl's *A Preface to Democratic Theory* (Chicago: University of Chicago Press, 1956), especially Chapter 2.

[14] Duncan Black's *The Theory of Committees and Elections* (Cambridge: Cambridge University Press, 1958) summarizes a good deal of the history involved, and also develops a number of intriguing political hypotheses about committee behavior from a simple algebraic theory.

*Arrow has generalized this result in the following way. He considers various possible "welfare functions," which assign *collective* preferential orderings of at least three social alternatives to all possible configurations of *individual* preference orderings. The policy alternatives may be candidates for President, conflicting foreign policies, or a different political constitution. The society is assumed to have at least two citizens.

*Arrow is interested in seeing if it is possible to solve for a unique welfare function that obeys reasonable criteria for collective choice very much like those introduced by Nash and discussed above. First he would require a "positive association of individual and social values" (a weaker version of the Pareto requirement), by which he means that the welfare function resulting from one individual's reordering his preferences in *favor* of an alternative X, while no others change their minds, should *not lower* this alternative in the collective ordering.

*He also would require an optimal social welfare function to obey the "independence of irrelevant alternatives." In the Threemanland example above, this criterion requires that, when a fourth constitutional possibility (e.g., Fascism) may also be voted on, collective orderings of the other three constitutions will not change.

*Finally, Arrow (and most but not all political theorists) would require an optimal welfare function that was neither dictatorial nor imposed. By dictatorial welfare functions, Arrow means those in which one individual has all his preferential orderings accepted, regardless of the preferences of other members of society. Imposed welfare functions, on the other hand, order alternatives like X and Y regardless of *all* possible combinations of individual orderings.

*Arrow then proves a result that shatters his preconceived notions of collective rationality:

Arrow's Impossibility Theorem. Any social welfare function defined in the above manner, showing a positive association of social and individual values, and independent of additional orderings of irrelevant alternatives will necessarily be either imposed from outside a society or dictatorially determined within it.[15]

Arrow's theorem is important particularly because its logic is impeccable. It challenges believers in democracy to restate their assump-

[15] See Luce and Raiffa's discussion and proof in Chapter 14 of *Games and Decisions* for further details. The crux of the proof is that a minimum set of individuals *within* a society that determine the collective preference between two alternatives must act as a dictator if the voters' paradox is never allowed to occur.

tions in more consistent forms. Given a desire that collective choices should depend on the wishes of more than one citizen in a society, analysts of politics must find what conditions are necessary for rational collective choices to occur.

SOME POSSIBLE REPLIES. Several comments may stimulate the reader to further reflection.[16] First, perhaps it is too much to suggest that collective choices order more than two alternatives at a time. Two-party democracy requires no more; schemes of proportional representation do not escape this dilemma. Unfortunately, however, Black has shown that winning candidates or policies in repeated either-or decisions are not always the absolute favorite of a democratic majority; they depend heavily on the *order* in which pairs of alternatives are presented for selection.

Secondly, it has been discovered that majority voting procedures insure transitive collective preferences only when policy preferences can be ranked by every voter along *the same* unidimensional continuum of alternatives (which might be a line starting at the left with communism, then socialism, and so on until fascism would appear at the far right). Along this continuum, preferences for each voter must be "single peaked"—maximum at one point and less and less desirable as he moves farther from it in either direction. The citizens of Three-manland, for example, cannot be ranked in this fashion. (Try it!) With ordinal measurement of utilities, a "consensual ordering" of the main issues facing a society, an "agreement to disagree" in a certain way, is terribly unlikely. Does it in fact ever occur?

Finally, it should have been noticed by the reader that *Nash's cooperative solution to partly competitive games, including the prisoners' dilemma, appears to give exactly the opposite result to Arrow's impossibility theorem.* Both use criteria of the independence of irrelevant alternatives, and both employ a version of Pareto optimality. Why then do the differences occur?

A realistic solution of this apparent contradiction may be possible *if* preference orderings are assumed measurable on an interval scale. Both the von Neumann-Morgenstern theory (see footnote 5) and Nash's

[16] Additional references may be found in Luce and Raiffa, *op. cit.*, Chapter 14; two bibliographical articles in the *American Political Science Review:* Richard Fagen, "Some Contributions of Mathematical Reasoning to the Study of Politics," and William H. Riker's "Voting and the Summation of Preferences," both of which appear in **55,** 4 (December 1961). A readable book length exposition of related problems is James M. Buchanan and Gordon Tullock, *The Calculus of Consent; Logical Foundations of Constitutional Democracy* (Ann Arbor: University of Michigan Press, 1962).

Theorem assume interval measures of utility, while Arrow does not. Multidimensional politics along several "left-right" continua (economic liberalism, civil rights, and foreign affairs, for example) would no longer be a problem; a single-dimension "consensual ordering" of alternatives need not be required. Multidimensionally, a rational collective ranking of policy alternatives would be possible if each individual's preferences along several different dimensions (e.g., in Threemanland, attitudes toward capitalism and toward democracy) were measured on an interval scale about some socially accepted or morally prescribed disagreement point. The basic normative political questions would then become (1) what influence should everyone be conceded before collective bargaining takes place; (2) what weights should be given in the collective ranking to the preferences of various individuals and collectivities; and (3) which preference dimensions, for whom and to what extent, are relevant to the particular set of alternatives being considered.

Interpersonal comparisons of this kind are always controversial, but the collective decisions (authoritative value allocations) made by societies do *in fact* take these factors unequally into account.[17] Therefore it does not seem *impossible* for political philosophy to compare and evaluate various empirical alternatives in terms of clearly stated and operational value norms of a non-dictatorial sort.

CONCLUSION. Theories of political behavior should serve what Karl Deutsch has summarized as predictive, mensurative, organizing, and heuristic functions.[18] Like several of the mathematical theories previously discussed, game theory performs each of these functions.

If individuals follow its prescribed strategies, game theory makes predictions about human behavior when complete or nearly complete information is available. Its moral prescriptions will prove to be accurate predictions, however, only when players continue to follow the same sets of rules and the utilities in the payoff matrices do not change.

Game theory's contributions to political measurement are considerable. First, it suggests a rigorous and plausible experimental way of measuring individual utilities at interval levels of accuracy. Power, fairly or unfairly exercised, can also be measured in a game theoretical

---

[17] Warren Miller and Donald Stokes, "Constituency Influence in Congress," *American Political Science Review,* **57,** 1 (March 1963), pp. 45–56, is a pioneering empirical study in this regard. It shows that constituency members appear to affect their congressmen's decisions on some issues, e.g., civil rights, but not on others, e.g., foreign affairs.

[18] Karl W. Deutsch, *The Nerves of Government* (New York: The Free Press of Glencoe, 1963).

way when alternative intentions and utilities are taken into account. In two-person zero-sum situations, potential power may be interpreted as the "value" of the game.[19]

By the organizing function of theories, Deutsch means their ability to bring together, in a deductive fashion if possible, a wide range of experience. As a formal, content-free language, admirably suited to unambiguous logical manipulation, mathematics should continue to organize and combine, in unexpected fashions, man's rational and irrational experience. Certainly this is true of von Neumann's exploration of the meaning of optimal rational behavior in competitive situations, and of later work by Nash and Arrow on the meaning of the collective interest.

Whether mathematical ways of empirically and normatively analyzing politics will suggest new ideas and new explanations, as heuristic theories of politics should do, depends substantially on the relevance of their concepts to political behavior and on the attitudes of investigators using them. As better means for measuring utilities, describing and prescribing optimal strategies in conflict situations, game theory is of particular relevance, even if only as an intellectual standard in terms of which less rational and less informed behavior may be described. In conjunction and dialogue with less formalized approaches, mathematical theories of collective decision-making will continue to contribute to the already substantial insights provided by mathematical analyses of politics.

[19] Other important game theoretic approaches to the measurement of formal and informal power are Shapley and Shubik, "A Method for Evaluating the Distribution of Power in a Committee System," and John C. Harsanyi, "Measurement of Social Power," both in Shubik (ed.), *op. cit.*

APPENDIX

Political Judgment and Statistical Significance

ARISTOTLE SHOWED the necessity of universal laws in explaining political events. His syllogisms were also useful in logically deducing statements from others of even more general validity. He did not develop, however, a systematic set of procedures for establishing these universal laws, or the laws from which they themselves were derived.

At the cost of introducing uncertainty into explanations, modern inductive statistics has developed systematic and explicit methods for establishing and testing empirical generalizations. Some of the descriptive tools used in this process have already been reviewed in previous chapters on measuring inequality and statistical correlation. How such findings can be used in making generalizations, however, has been left to a discussion in this appendix.

Modern inductive statistics has been described as the science of decision-making under uncertainty. It provides sophisticated ways of calculating the risks involved in generalizing from incomplete information. Since practicing politicians must also repeatedly generalize about the chances of success and failure of certain policies, they, too, are specialists in risky decision-making. Showing this correspondence between statisticians and politicians may serve both to awaken in those who are politically minded an interest in statistics and to make clearly apparent the elements of value judgment involved in every statistical decision.

A Hypothetical Example

Failures of inference and judgment can be summarized as sins of omission and commission: either we accept falsehoods or reject the truth. The following practical but oversimplified example illustrates how risks of both omission and commission can be calculated.

Assume that the administrator of a scientific department would like to promote a technical innovation among medical practitioners. He is convinced of the new method's superiority, but is uncertain whether, even with an intensive and costly effort, he will be able to convince at least a majority of the medical profession. He is particularly worried that a two-thirds majority of the medical profession might come out against him and seriously damage his career.

An advisory panel of six members of the medical profession, picked randomly to insure their representativeness, is available for consultation. Leaving aside the many other problems involved, the administrator wants to gauge the likely response of the medical profession from the responses of the panel. He decides to risk going ahead if and only if all six panel members support him.

Statistical Significance

What are the risks he is taking? Perhaps he will be wrong to go ahead even with the panel's support. How likely would he be to go ahead with his proposal on the basis of the panel's unanimous approval if his pessimistic hypothesis (that he would get only one-third support) was actually correct?[1] Statisticians refer to this uncertainty as the probability of a type I error: of *rejecting a hypothesis that is actually true.* The probability of making this sin of commission is usually known as the level of statistical significance associated with a specific procedure for deciding when to reject a particular hypothesis.

Statistically, it is possible for the administrator to find the level of significance associated with the unanimity procedure as a means of generalizing from a sample result to the unknown views of the medical profession.[2] To do so, he must hypothetically calculate the probability of getting unanimous panel opinions in *repeated random samples* of the medical profession. The necessary mathematical result is the binomial theorem:[3]

---

[1] Note that this pessimistic hypothesis may very well not be true—and the administrator knows it. Statisticians also work with hypothetical propositions, called *null hypotheses*, when they are trying to establish other explanatory relationships.

[2] Calculations of statistical significance are difficult or impossible unless the sample of relevant data has been randomly selected. In reality, of course, every member of the medical profession would not have an equal chance of advising the Federal government as we have assumed. Nonetheless, in doing actual research work, political and other social scientists often fail to allow for the unrepresentativeness of the opinions and facts they are studying before generalizing their conclusions.

This error of asserting statistical significance for unspecified universes from which samples have *not* been randomly drawn pervades informal *and* scientific political analysis. It applies to the simple techniques illustrated above as well as the corresponding ways in which the significance of χ^2's and r^2's can be tested. For some socio-political examples, see Leslie Kish, "Confidence Intervals for Complex Samples," *American Sociological Review*, **22**, (1957), pp. 154–165.

[3] This theorem is sometimes proved in advanced high school algebra courses but will not be derived here because of its length. Some users find its most valuable contribution to be in predicting the probability of different poker hands or of sequences of coin tosses. An excellent social science oriented derivation may be found in H. M. Blalock, Jr., *Social Statistics* (New York: McGraw-Hill, 1960), Chapters 9 and 10.

THE BINOMIAL THEOREM.   Assume an event may occur with a probability p. In N independent instances, the probability that it will occur exactly t times $[Pr(t)]$ is given by Equation (1):

$$Pr(t) \quad = \frac{N!}{t!(N-t)!} \quad \cdot \quad p^t(1-p)^{N-t} \tag{1}$$

Probability of = Number of   Times $\begin{pmatrix} \text{Probability of} \\ \text{any single instance} \end{pmatrix}$
t instances   orders in
                     which t
                     instances
                     may occur

In Equation (1) the terms with exclamation points after them are known as *factorials*. They represent products of a series of integers. $N!$, for example, is read as "N-factorial," and is defined as follows:

$$N! = N \cdot (N-1)(N-2) \cdots (3) \cdot (2) \cdot (1)$$

Thus 4! is $4 \cdot 3 \cdot 2 \cdot 1$ or 24; by convention both 0! and 1! equal 1.

Applying the binomial theorem to calculate the significance of the administrator's decision procedure is easy. N can be interpreted as the number of decisions made by the randomly selected panel members ($N = 6$). The probability p can be identified with the possibility of support from any panel member (p is assumed to be the same for all members of the medical profession, including the panel). The administrator is concerned with the significance of his decision procedure, i.e., the likelihood that unanimity would occur when p equals only 1/3. The chance of his being proved wrong corresponds to the probability of finding that all six doctors support the proposal, when each is assumed to make up his mind independently of the others, with a probability of support equal to only 1/3. In this case, unanimous support is obviously not likely, but how unlikely we are not sure. Putting numbers for N, r, p, and t into the binomial theorem (which applies only to independent events all with equal probability),

$$Pr(6 \text{ supporting votes}) = \frac{6!}{6!0!} \cdot \left(\frac{1}{3}\right)^1 \left(\frac{2}{3}\right)^0 = \left(\frac{1}{3}\right)^6$$

This expression equals $1/27 \cdot 1/27$, or $1/729$. *Thus the administrator's chances of committing himself to action when his pessimistic hypothesis is actually correct is extremely small*, equal approximately to one chance in a thousand.

The power of a statistical test

No politician, however, would automatically play it so safe in deciding to act according to a unanimity rule without also asking a related question. A kind of risk other than that associated with statistical significance is clearly involved: "How often would a majority of the medical profession favor the proposal even if their representatives were *not* unanimous?" It would be a real sin of omission not to pick up their support when it could easily have been obtained. Statisticians call the *failure to reject a false hypothesis* a type II error. The probability of a type II error is measured by a coefficient β, pronounced "beta." In the present case this would mean the probability, in repeated random samples of doctors, of not getting a unanimous panel even when a 50 percent majority of the medical profession favored his proposal.

The value of β depends on how false the hypothesis actually is. If 60 percent of the profession proved to be against the administrator's proposal, his pessimistic estimate of 67 percent would not have been far wrong. The results of his unanimity procedure, even when repeated several times, would probably not suggest to the administrator that his pessimistic hypothesis was wrong by 7 percent. If the actual opinions of the profession were evenly divided, however, his chances of obtaining panel unanimity would be slightly higher. It would be preferable for the administrator to have some chance of finding out by his panel experiment that his working hypothesis was 17 percent too pessimistic. The likelihood that his panel procedure would reject an overly pessimistic hypothesis (and *not* commit a type II error) is called the *power* of a statistical testing procedure.

Power of a test = $1 - \beta$ Probability of not making a type II error

The probability of the administrator's making a type II error would, of course, be larger than the extremely small significance level of his procedure, but its exact or relative magnitude is not obvious. Before continuing, the reader should try to estimate it by intuitive methods: politicians would at least make the attempt.

If the probability of support by each member of the profession was actually 1/2, how often would the administrator fail to realize this potential support? In other words, how often would the panel not unanimously favor something that each doctor had a 50–50 chance of supporting? In this case, the probability of failing to reject an overly pessimistic hypothesis would be the combined likelihood that less than six equivocal panel members gave the administrator support. Symbolically,

β = The probability of a type II error by the administrator
$$= P_r(0) + P_r(1) + P_r(2) + P_r(3) + P_r(4) + P_r(5)$$

Because the combined probability of all possible levels of support must equal unity, a simple but equivalent computation is possible: since $P_r(i)$'s for i = 1 through 6 add up to unity (all panel splits are taken into account), the probability of a type II error is simply:

$$\beta = 1 - P_r(6)$$

Using the binomial theorem, with p = 1/2 as the supposed true probability of each doctor's support,

$$\beta = 1 - \frac{6!}{6!0!} \left(\frac{1}{2}\right)^6 \left(\frac{1}{2}\right)^0 = 1 - \left(\frac{1}{2}\right)^6 = \frac{63}{64}$$

In showing so much caution by requiring panel unanimity before proceeding, the administrator has decided not to make his proposal in the rather likely case that the panel will not reach unanimity. The cost to him in opportunities foregone, however, is that *in 63 out of 64 similar situations he would be foregoing action that would lead at least to majority support by the medical profession!*

The same conclusion can be stated in terms of the *power of the unanimity procedure to reject a falsely pessimistic hypothesis.* In this case the panel procedure will only succeed when unanimity occurs.

$$\text{The power of the panel procedure} = P_r(6) = \frac{1}{64}$$

In only 1 out of 64 similar situations could the administrator expect the panel unanimously to support him, even when there was a 0.5 probability that each member of the medical profession (themselves included) would do so.

SUMMARY. Many of the aspects of this example would properly be questioned by political observers as extremely oversimplified. The point of the argument, however, is that two kinds of probability, risks of commission and omission, and the costs associated with each, should be assessed for decision procedures in both practical and theoretical politics. Whenever more representative samples of information can be obtained or inferred, they should help in such an assessment.

But, for any given set of data, small significance levels can only be assured by also decreasing the learning power of the test procedure. If new knowledge can be learned only by risking a rejection of conventional wisdom, politicians and political analysts need to consider both the statistical power and the statistical significance of their decision procedures.